FROM PATIE

HOW TO TURN YOUR DENTAL PRACTICE INTO A CASH COW (IN 12 MONTHS OR LESS!)

(A Step-By-Step Guide to Getting <u>More</u> Patients … Making <u>More</u> Money … and Enjoying Your Work <u>More</u>!!)

Written by: Dr. Woody Oakes

Table of Contents

Chapter One:
Not Every Patient Is Equal: How Patient Demographics Can
Define Your Practice..9

Chapter Two:
Getting The Patients You Want And Deserve 15

Chapter Three:
The Importance Of A Solid Marketing Plan..............................25

Chapter Four:
Increasing Your Profitability...45

Chapter Five:
Increasing Your Bottom Line By Controlling Overhead
Costs...57

Chapter Six:
Convert Calls Into Cash...69

Chapter Seven:
Scheduling For Success 83

Chapter Eight:
Learning How To Motivate Your Office 95

Chapter Nine:
Managing For Success 107

Chapter Ten:
Getting The Most From Your Hygiene Department.................117

Chapter Eleven:
Incorporating New Technologies Into Your Practice.............125

Chapter Twelve:
Getting Control Of Your Office Finances.................................131

Chapter Thirteen:
Exit Strategies: How To Plan For Your Retirement................141

Chapter Fourteen:
The Profitable Partnership..153
ONE FINAL THOUGHT...163

INTRODUCTION

You knew that building a solid dental practice wouldn't be easy. But, did you ever dream that it would cost this much emotionally and physically? If you're tired of working long days, late nights and even weekends, only to realize that neither your practice – nor your profits – are growing like they should, then it may be time for a change.

If you're ready to spend less time chairside... earn more money ... and enjoy your work again, then keep reading. We're going to show you exactly how to improve your practice significantly in less than 12 months. By this time next year, you'll be spending more time with your family doing the things you used to enjoy; earning bigger profits and experiencing much less stress at work than you are today. Big changes are on the way – the question is: *are you ready for them?*

It's time to take the lead and grow your practice into the thriving business you know it can be. Hundreds of other dentists across the nation have done it and you can too! The guidance found within the pages of this book have all been tried – and deemed successful – by others in your field. As a matter-of-fact, they are directly derived from the famed Mega Coaching Club, which has been helping dentists just like you for years grow their practices and begin enjoying the professional and personal benefits a more streamlined business can offer.

Most of the Mega Coaching Club's clients find their profits increasing within the first few months of the program, even while they begin to scale back their working hours. How? By starting at the front door of their dental practice and learning to streamline every aspect of their office straight to the back door.

This guide will begin by teaching you how to fix all of the external facets of your practice that may be hurting – or at least not enhancing – your image, to finding the right kind of patients; offering the services your patients want and need most; learning how to close more cases; as well as finding better ways to motivate your staff.

Sound simple enough? Well, it isn't. Change can be difficult for some people, and incorporating the depth of change this program may call for can seem unnatural at first. But, we think – no, we *know,* that once you see the affects changing the way you do business can have on your life, your staff and your patients, you'll understand how important it really can be to building the kind of dental practice you've always dreamed of.

Divided into three main sections covering the outside things you can do to change your practice; the internal aspects affecting your business, as well as ways to move forward to the next stage of your practice (and your life), *"Turning Your Dental Practice into a Thriving Business in Just One Year,"* is designed to take you, dear doctor, through every phase of making your practice everything you ever dreamed it could be. Chockfull of practical tips and advice, it is the guide's aim to answer all of your questions regarding:
- Patient Demographics and bringing in a continuous flow of the right kind of patients
- Establishing a Solid Marketing Plan
- Increasing Your Bottom Line
- Controlling Overhead Costs
- Converting Every Call Into a Scheduled Appointment
- Scheduling Dilemmas
- Motivating Your Staff
- Incorporating New Technologies Into Your Practice
- Handling Office Finances
- Developing an Exit Strategy including Selling Off Partnership
- And More.... Much More ...

By considering each of these issues as a single spoke in the wheel driving your office into the future, the guide will show you how to develop your spokes in the right sequence and in the right way in order to create a wheel that is able to take your practice on a journey aimed at success!

Sound ambitious? It is! But I guarantee that it's going to be a great ride – and one well worth taking. Now, take one last look at your dental practice. This may be the last time you see it as it is right now. By the time we're done, you may hardly recognize it (or your staff). No matter where your practice is today, be prepared to be amazed at where, and what, it is exactly one year from now. Even the smallest practices that have utilized the ideas found in this book have as much as doubled their profits within the first 12 months. Ready to get started? Great! First, let's learn more about the patients you have now, and how to fill your chairs with more of the ones that'll enhance your practice and make your business grow...

Chapter One:

Not Every Patient Is Equal:

How Patient Demographics Can Define Your Practice

Most dentists agree that their offices would run just perfectly if it weren't for the patients. Sure, your patients may be the ones making your office run; but that doesn't mean that your patients should be the ones running your practice!

Imagine your prefect patient. The odds are he/she would be someone who:
- Pays for treatment on time – every time!
- Appreciates the quality of work you offer!
- Trusts your treatment suggestions – and accepts all of them!
- Respects your time and shows up on time – Every Time!
- Feels compelled to refer their friends and family to your practice!

Now, imagine your chairs filled with patients just like the one described above. Wouldn't your days be a lot less stressful and a lot more productive – not to mention lucrative, if your appointment calendar was filled with this type of patient? Sound like a pipe dream? It doesn't have to be. Unless you are striving to solicit the right kind of patients, you are missing a wonderful opportunity to make your office run like it's meant to, and to service the type of patient you've been dreaming about.

Where do you find this type of quality patient? They may be a lot closer than you think. There are several ways to build your practice with the kinds of patients you want and deserve:
- **Your Existing Files.** Most doctors have no idea how many downright fantastic patients have been

left to become inactive in their practice. It is estimated that the average one-doctor practice has at least 500-1,000 inactive files gathering dust in their cabinets. Those are patients who already know you, are reasonably comfortable with you and have trusted you with their care in the past – all ingredients for a solid doctor/patient relationship – and more profits!

- **New Residents To Your Area.** People move from area to area a lot these days, making it more important than ever to be the first one to make contact with new residents in order to grow your dental practice. Being the first one to welcome them to the area; introduce them to their new community; and make your services known are an important way to make new residents remember your name and feel comfortable enough to transfer their records to your practice.

- **Target The Patients Most Qualified For Your Practice.** You may think that you need to prove your qualifications to potential patients, but have you ever considered making sure that a new patient is qualified to join your clientele? Targeting your marketing to support your efforts to gain qualified patients who meet your own criteria is the best way to add just the kind of patients that will enhance your practice and not cause undo stress and work. Sending out a mass mailing aimed at everyone in the area, and not targeting specific patient groups, may indeed result in a number of new patients, but you must consider if they are the right kind of patients.

- **Staying In Contact With The Patients You Already Have.** Many dentists make the mistake to believe that, "once a patient, always a patient." That philosophy can cause dramatic ebbs and flows in your scheduling and patient acquisition. As you will soon learn, working to keep the patients you already have can be just as important as working hard to add new patients to your active files.

Now that you know the importance of enticing the right new patients into your practice (and keeping the right old ones), you may be wondering how to figure out *who* these perfect patients are.

Taking A Good Look At Your Patient Demographics

Now is the time to take a good look at your current patient files to figure out who you are serving – and why. Let's say for instance, that you want to begin offering orthodontic care, but the vast majority of your patients are over the age of 50 with older children. The odds are you are going to have an uphill climb to changing your practice toward a younger clientele without a lot of hard work and strategic marketing. That doesn't mean that you can't expand into orthodontics, it just means that it will be harder and take longer to get that type of patient through your door.

So, before you begin thinking about the types of patients you want to lure into your practice in the future, or even the services you'd like to provide, let's take a good look at your current patient demographics and see how you can work with what you already have to expand into more realistic areas of patient care.

Some of the things you'll be looking for when running your demographics are:
- The age of your practice (are there too many older people; too many younger people; too many uninsured people?)
- Do your current patients fit your ideal patient profile – why or why not?
- What is the average income of your patients, and does this meet with your own patient profile criteria? For example, if you want to offer more cosmetic dentistry services, but 90% of your patients make less than $30,000 a year and are uninsured, the odds are good you won't have much luck in expanding into this area of service without drastically changing your patient demographics.

Once you see where your service niche is today, and where you'd like it to be in the months and years to come, you'll have a better idea of what you will need to change within your practice right now to entice those "ideal" patients, and how to go about doing it.

The first thing you will need to do is gather whatever criteria your mailing house will need to design a solid mailing list for you with only the names of those people in your area who would be most interested in the types of services you do (and want to) offer. For instance, if you want to expand into offering implant services, you'll want the mailing list you use to only contain the names of people who would be interested in (and could afford) this type of service.

Next, you will want to design a mailing piece specifically geared toward that group of people using only the graphics, message and headline most apt to attract them.
The net result of better targeting your marketing efforts will be a more quality patient, and this will result in less stress and more money for you and your office staff! After all, if you're happy, the odds are they'll be happy and if you're making more money, they will too.

Using The Strategies That Work
Can the simple act of getting to know who you are treating – and who you would like to treat – and gearing your services toward that audience really bring in the number and quality of patients that you want and tend to thrive? Of course it can! It may seem to make sense to grab any patient you can in the early days of your practice, but if you don't take the time and energy to streamline your services and go after those patients you most want to treat, you'll find yourself (and your practice) struggling to survive, working too many hours, for far too little money with little or no gain in the future.

Now, let's learn how to reach the people we've discussed in this chapter with the most innovative marketing strategies out there. Let's begin by learning how to reach out to old patients; invite new move-ins to join your practice; target those in need of the services you are currently offering and those you want to offer in the future; and how to stay in tune to your current patient base and their needs; all in an effort to grow the type of practice you've always wanted.

Chapter Two:

Getting the Patients You Want and Deserve

Reactivating Previous Patients

The first step to filling your scheduling calendar with good patient prospects is to take a good hard look at your patient files. Few doctors realize the potential hidden in those drawers.

With the American Dental Association (ADA), estimating the cost of acquiring every new patient to be around $100 (or more), it is obviously cheaper to reactivate existing patients than trying to solicit new ones.

Don't think that you have enough inactive files to bring in the number of patients you need to prosper and grow your practice? Think again! The average single doctor practice has hundreds of files featuring good quality patients that haven't seen the inside of your office in years. Larger practices have even more! Before you can even begin to entice them back to your office, you first must acknowledge that they exist, and then get them back from your file drawers and into your active files once again.

Reactivating stale files will require a team effort on the part of your entire staff – that includes your receptionist, scheduling coordinator, and even your hygienists. Depending on whether you go through your files by hand, or have your technical support staff handle it, the process could take anywhere from a few weeks to a few months. Once you have figured out who you have not seen in awhile, each of these past patients will need to be contacted several times (more on that in a minute). That kind of effort will take teamwork. So get ready to motivate your staff and get them on board with this important marketing strategy.

Getting A Good Look At Your Inactive Files

The first step to reactivating some of those patients is to redefine what you consider "inactive." Most doctors consider a patient who hasn't been into the office in 2 years to be "inactive," while most retention experts agree that once a patient has waited 12 months for a revisit, then they have either moved onto another practice or have decided to withhold treatment for some reason. That's why it's so important to keep in touch with patients by the 12th month.

If indeed a patient hasn't been into your office in 12 months, 18 months, or even longer for care, have you lost them forever? Not necessarily. Many doctors have discovered that a simple postcard is enough to bring past patients back in the office.

So, the first step to reactivating forgotten patients is to go through your files one at a time and write down the name, address and brief patient history of anyone you haven't seen in the last year. If handling this assignment by hand, it is best to give each member of your staff a different letter of the alphabet to make sure that no patient is missed. This, of course can take quite a bit of time, so everyone in the office will need to get involved in order to go through the files in a timely manner.

Most offices experience down times at certain times of the day, week, month and even year. These are great times to go through files. For example, if bad weather is causing a lot of cancellations, get your staff working on those files. If a hygienist finds herself with a vacant appointment slot, get her working on these files. Any free time should be spent going through old patient files until the list is complete!

If, however, you have a good software customer support system service, you may want to have them compile the information you need from your digital files, and have your staff go through only older paper files by hand. This can be a lot quicker and a lot less hassle, although electronic files may not give you as detailed information regarding a patient as paper ones. Simply explain what you are doing to the support technician and ask him/her to run a report of patients who have not been seen by your office in the last 12 months. While you're at it, have them do something called a merge purge which will give you a list of inactive patients by household (and not just names), to help alleviate sending four postcards to the same address for four different family members.

Use specially designed postcards to help you better understand if a patient believes they are still in your practice; have moved onto another office; is even still living in the area; and whether or not they would like to schedule a new appointment. To get a response, you will need to include their name, address, and the date of their last visit on the card. Research has shown that handwriting these postcards and mailing them with a live stamp will result in four times the response than using address labels and a bulk-mailing stamp.

It's important to get these postcards in the mail as soon as possible, so assign the project to one coordinator who will work with the rest of your staff to meet whatever deadline you impose (two months should give everyone enough time to collect the data needed and to address 1,000 or so cards for mailing).

Once the postcards go out, you can realistically expect to hear back from about 70% of those patients. Of course, not all of them will call to make appointments. Some will let you know that they've found a new dentist or aren't interested in returning to your practice. We'll discuss how to woo back some of these patients in a future chapter. For now, you simply want to concentrate on those who do decide to make a new appointment by improving patient relations and care, which we will discuss in detail in the second half of the book.

Of course there will be about 30% of people that do not respond to your postcard inquiry. Although a bit tougher to woo back to your practice, it is not impossible. Start by sending a reactivation letter. It's a great tool to use to get back the last group of people on your inactive list.

Turning Your Attention To Finding New Patients
One of the first things we'll discuss when it comes to finding new patients is some sort of mass mailing. Unless you want to waste a lot of money on printing and postage, you will need to streamline your mailing list to solicit the right kind of patients. That's why it is so important to sign up for a good zip code search that has the capabilities to highlight new move-ins to your area, as well as people who fit specific criteria.

Let's begin with new move-ins. Although you may think that you can only contact people within your own zip code, most dentists discover when contacting new residents that they can solicit business from patients as far away as 20 miles and three zip codes. People are willing to drive for good service, especially when it comes to dentistry.

With that in mind, have your zip code service send you a monthly list of new move-ins within your target areas. For some of you living in smaller rural areas, this may mean only a handful of welcome/informational postcards to send out each month, while those in higher density areas may find yourself sending 1,000 or more.

Now, keep in mind that it can take up to 3-4 contacts before a new patient picks up the phone and calls for more information or to make an appointment. That is why most marketing experts agree that you should send a new postcard every month for at least three months (preferable five or six), to every new resident on your list. Certainly, this type of approach takes some time and effort to garner results – but it does work. Dentists who've tried this approach have managed to successfully pull in as much as 50% of the new residents of their area as long-term patients.

Why target new residents? The answers are simple:
•   They are the easiest people to reach

- They are not currently seeing a dentist
- They need to find care fairly quickly
- Most importantly, they are not another problem or dissatisfied patient

What happens if you try this approach for a few months and nothing happens? The first step to increasing your response rate is to change postcards. The fact is, not every marketing piece will work in every area with every type of patient. Being willing to experiment with postcards that work for the clientele in rural Kansas vs. another dentist in New York is very important, which leads us to recognize the importance of knowing who your patients are, and who you'd like to attract to your office in the future.

Using Your Business Cards To Bring In Business
One of the simplest and cheapest marketing tools at your disposal may be your business card. Some dentists aren't comfortable handing out their cards, but you really need to get over that. This mini-billboard is a great way to let people know about the services that you offer. But first, you must design a great card.

Want to increase your success rate by 500%? Use a photo card instead of the standard black and white special like everyone else that features a picture of yourself; your staff; or even your office. This will create a business card that people will want to keep.

Why use a photo? There are several reasons:
- They are different, and anything different will get more attention
- People hate to throw away pictures, so they are more apt to keep your card for future use
- They can make you and your staff seem more friendly and accessible
- They work!

Studies have repeatedly shown that photo business cards can be 100-500% more successful than traditional cards, so why not use them to your own benefit?

The second thing you need to consider when creating your business card is to make sure that it speaks to your target audience. Consider the type of patient you are trying to connect with and use fonts, graphics and styles that fit that target group.

For instance, one of the biggest mistakes business owners make is using a too-small font for their phone number, especially when their target audience is older. If you specialize in dentures and implants, you'd better be sure that your office number can be read by someone in that age bracket without hunting for their eyeglasses!

Once you have designed a fantastic card, you'll need to use them. Sure, handing out cards to everyone you meet is one way (and does work well for some people), but it isn't the only way to properly utilize your cards. Here are a few more tips:

- Allow your staff to hand out office cards with a handwritten note on the back offering 10% off of a service, a free whitening session, etc.
- Write a quick thank you note on the back of one of your cards to the waitress when you go out to eat and leave it along with a big tip; not only will she remember you, she'll likely tell others about the friendly dentist who took the time to thank them for a job well done
- Slip a card in the envelope with every bill you pay
- Slip a card into your DVD rentals and or library books before returning them
- Place a business card in every form of correspondence you mail
- Ask your patients to pass them along to family and friends

While business cards may seem very insignificant to many, the fact is they can be one of the most cost effective ways to introduce people to you and your practice!

Dental Emergency Stickers

Another marketing tool that can be used quite successfully to pull in new patients is the use of very inexpensive stickers that feature something simple like "Dental Emergency and your phone number." You don't even need to include your name. Costing literally a penny or less for each one, you can ask your staff to place these stickers on every payphone, telephone pole and bulletin board around town. Within days your phone number can be plastered in hundreds of locations, giving more people than ever access to your services. Consider this: by placing this simple advertising sticker on the payphones at a local hotel, whom do you think a guest with a toothache is going to call? That's right – YOU!

Worried that people will find these stickers annoying or offensive? Don't. It is rare for anyone to call the number to complain, and if they do, be sure to offer them some sort of compromise or free service to smooth over their complaints.

Don't Forget Those You Are Already Treating

Many doctors spend so much time and effort trying to bring new patients into their practice they sometimes forget the importance of remembering the ones they already have. No patient should be taken for granted whether they have been with your office for 10 minutes ... or ten years.

The ADA has recently reported a study showing that dentists who do not make an effort to keep in contact with their patients every month risk losing them to another practice. The odds are you are already sending out birthday, anniversary and holiday greetings as well as appointment reminders to your current patients. Why not take that strategy a step further and send a monthly newsletter or profitable postcard that features interesting facts, dental tips, recipes, savings strategies or more. Remember, more than 82% of all dental appointments are made by women, so you'd better be sure that whatever correspondence you send out appeals to women's interests and needs.

One of the reasons this type of postcard works so well is because a very small part talks about dentistry. Most people aren't interested in dentistry like we in the industry are, so it's important to give them valuable tips and advice on things they do care about.

One important trick to making these postcards successful is including information that someone wouldn't want to throw away: a great website; a tasty recipe; a good quote; etc.

At a cost of less than $6.00 a year per household, these postcards give you monthly access to each and every one of your patients and keeps your name and practice at the forefront of their thoughts should a dental emergency arise.

Patient Calls
One of the easiest and best ways to make your patients think you are the best dentist in the world is to simply show them that you care. Patient calls are a good way to express concern over a patient as well as to establish trust with them. Plus it can help you tackle any problem right away; making it much easier to smooth over hurt feelings or turn a bad situation around before it negatively affects your relationship with the patient.

For instance, by simply calling a patient that evening or the next day after they have undergone a more serious procedure can help you bond better with the patient; express your concern as well as check for small problems before they become big ones. One dentist explained how one of these simple two-minute calls might have prevented a lawsuit when he discovered a patient bleeding unnaturally following a procedure. Thinking the bleeding was normal; the patient herself did not call the office and only discovered a problem when the dentist called her to check on her progress. Not only was the patient grateful for his diligence but now considers him an outstanding doctor that she feels free to recommend to anyone who needs his care.

Being Available Even When The Office Is Closed
Offering 24-hour availability can be another big plus is
retaining patients. One of the top five reasons why people
leave a dental practice is the inability to contact the dentist
in an emergency. Now, this doesn't mean that you have to
be willing to go into the office at 3 a.m. to handle a
problem, but it does mean making yourself available by
telephone to answer their questions and reassure them that
their problem can wait until the office reopens in the
morning. It can be very frustrating to have a problem and
not be able to get hold of anyone for help, so be sure to
offer an emergency number, your cell phone or even your
pager number to patients during off hours, and check your
messages regularly. If you're worried that people will
abuse the courtesy, don't. Most people are very respectful
of a doctor's family time and tend not to call with
unnecessary concerns.

As you can see, there are literally dozens of ways to expand
your practice simply by reactivating previous patients;
luring in new ones and remembering to appreciate the ones
that you already have.

Learning to market your services correctly is vital to
creating the practice that you are after. In the next chapter
we will discuss the importance of developing a solid
marketing plan for your future, as well as basic tips on
getting the job done right.

Chapter Three:

The Importance of a Solid Marketing Plan

The odds are that you have heard about the importance of marketing your practice before. But, has anyone ever really taught you *how* to do it? Well, we're going to right now!

What Marketing Can Do For You

All-too-often, marketing sounds too much like selling your services. Few dentists have the talent (or the stomach) for sales, and why should they? After all, they are doctors who have spent their time and energy learning how to help people. The problem is, if no one knows how good you are at what you do, they won't even know they should – let alone want – to walk into your office. A good quality marketing plan can help bridge the gap between patient and doctor and increase the awareness of your services for those who need you the most.

The first question you may have is what is marketing? More than simple sales techniques, marketing is a way for you to get to know patient prospects – and for them to get to know you and your services.

We've talked a lot about patient postcards thus far, and while an important marketing strategy to bringing in both old and new patients, it is only one spoke of that wheel we talked about earlier.

Branding And Logos

Consistency is a key when developing any type of marketing plan. That means everything you do to market your practice must contain the same look, and style. From your outdoor sign, yellow pages ad, and website to your postcards and newsletter, it must all feature the same logo or brand.

So, what is branding and how can it help to increase your business?

The concept of product branding began more than 100 years ago as a way for manufacturers to get a leg up on their competition. Through a direct marketing campaign they managed to convince consumers those brand name products and services were better than their generic counterparts. Suddenly generic off-brands were considered to be of lesser quality. This important marketing ploy not only succeeded, but has lasted over the last century, moving from manufacturing goods to every type of service available – including dentistry.

Not only does branding allow service providers to tap into more markets, but it also allows them to command higher fees. So, why are patients willing to pay the dental practice down the street featuring a well-known (and advertised) –franchise-named practice twice what they'll pay you? Because they've been convinced that he's worth more simply because of the logo attached to his name.

How can you compete with these so-called high-end franchises? Simple. Use the same strategy in your marketing efforts: develop your own brand and logo.

Once you have developed a brand and/or logo, you will notice your advertising efforts becoming more fruitful. After all, consumers are more apt to buy products and services they've been led to believe are "bigger and better."

Now that you understand the importance of branding and logos, it is time to select one for your own practice. When picking a brand name or logo remember these basic tips:
- **Choose Something That Can Survive The Test Of Time.** Don't try and be too "modern" with your brand name or logo. What is popular today will likely appear old and outdated soon. Instead, choose something that can weather the changes ahead.

- **Make Sure It Fits You.** The logo you pick will give prospective patients their first impression of who you are, so make sure that it clearly reflects your identity, tone, and service. Otherwise you may be stuck with a logo that doesn't tell anybody anything about who you are and what you offer.
- **Choose Colors Wisely.** Be sure to choose colors that appeal to your client base. For instance, a pediatric dentist will likely want to choose bold bright primary colors, while a geriatric dentist may opt for calmer, quieter more muted jewel tones.
- **Be Sure It Works In All Sizes.** Whatever logo you choose, remember it will likely be enlarged and reduced for use on a lot of different things: your business cards, stationery, invoices/bills; newsletters, signage, advertising, brochures, etc. Be sure it looks good (and can be seen) no matter what size it ends up being.
- **Hire A Professional.** This is not the time to be cheap and try and do it yourself. Creating a logo that will stand the test of time and offer some insight into your dental services while still being practical and pleasing to the eye, as well as entice potential patients, is better left to the professionals. Hire a good advertising or public relations agency to help you. If you can't afford an agency, at least head to your local art school or college to see if you can hire a student to design your new logo.
- **Get Lots Of Feedback.** Before heading off to the printer to start reproducing your new logo on all of your new marketing materials, be sure that it is going to do the job you're looking for. The only way to do this is to show to as many people as you can (other professionals, family, friends, neighbors, current patients, and more). Get as much feedback as you can to make sure it really is the right logo for you and your practice.

Once you have a new brand name or logo in place, it's time to incorporate it into every other aspect of your marketing plan.

Your Outdoor Sign
Let's begin with one of the most important marketing tools you can use: outdoor signage. The odds are most of you have settled for having your name listed on the outside sign of your office complex, with maybe a listing inside the front door. Unfortunately, being lumped in with the names of a lot of other doctors and service providers isn't doing much to rein in new patients. Think of it this way, do you ever read the signs outside of business buildings unless you're looking for a specific office? I didn't think so.

Believe it or not, adding something as simple as your own outdoor sign to your building or even office window can help generate a dozen new patient calls a week. Amazing! And the best news is that once you invest in a good sign you won't have to replace it for years, or even decades!

Vanity Phone Numbers
Vanity phone numbers are very inexpensive, yet can have a tremendous return for your practice. They're catchy and easy to remember: an essential ingredient to any marketing strategy.

The fact is, it's much easier to remember something that spells out a name or phrase than it is to remember a few random numbers. Now, I'm not suggesting that you immediately drop your current phone number. What I am suggesting is that you add another phone line for the time being that can be used with your promotional materials.

This will accomplish two things:
  1. It will help you more easily transition your current patients to the new number
  2. It will help you gauge the success of your marketing plan.

So what type of vanity number should you look for? Some of the top ones to check for availability include GRIN, SMILE, DENTIST, TOOTH, and ZOOM (if you offer Zoom whitening).

Your odds of getting GRIN are the best since it only has four letters. This puts the mathematical odds in your favor. The first step to acquiring a new vanity number is to call the local phone company, tell them you are a dentist and say that you would like to see if the following vanity phone numbers are available.

Now, in the event the number you really want is unavailable, take this tip from a dentist in rural Mississippi. When the phone company told him that all of his vanity choices were taken, he actually dialed the number he wanted most, which was his prefix and GRIN and he offered to pay the household who had it $250 to buy her number. The housewife he got on the line was ecstatic. She didn't care what phone number she ended up with – especially for $250! Now, this is the same doctor who initially thought getting a vanity number was a stupid idea. Now he gets as many as 5-6 new patient calls every week, just because of that number! Keep in mind that in most cases, you will not have to pay for your number of choice. The phone company will give it to you for free.

Yellow Pages Ads
Now, there seems to be some disagreement as to whether or not spending the money on a Yellow Pages ad is really worth the cost. The fact is, the vast majority of people looking for a new dentist do not find them in the phone book; they ask the people they know for referrals or look at other advertising medium for options. Still, there are a few who use the old stand-by: the Yellow Pages. Because of this, many dentists still believe it prudent to pay for these pricey annual ads.

Our suggestion here is a simple one. If you spend the money on one of these high-priced ads, you'd better be sure you are getting a darned good one! Be sure that the graphics are smart, the font is readable, and your placement is impeccable. Otherwise you just may be wasting money.

Newsletters

As we've already discussed, newsletters can be a great way to keep in touch with your patients, and even entice new ones to your practice. Sending out a quarterly newsletter chockfull of useful home tips and dental advice to your target mailing list can be a great way to introduce yourself to the community and keep your name in the forefront of their mind. Something as simple as a one-page tip sheet may be enough to accomplish your goal. Just make sure that it is filled with articles, recipes and tips that people will want to read (and keep).

Using Old Fashioned PR Tactics To Your Advantage

Public relations experts have been using a variety of PR tactics for years to benefit their clients. Some of the most basic (and easiest to implement) ideas include:

Using Articles To Gain Notoriety

One of the best marketing tools available today is newspaper articles. Getting articles published in your local newspaper is a great way to share your knowledge with the community and set yourself up as an expert in the field.

People turn to newspapers and television to find answers to their questions – even their dental ones.

Expert articles can be written as an "advertorial," (a paid placement that resembles all of the other "real" articles featured in the publication), or as a press release that is used to announce a new product, new service or other newsworthy event.

One important thing to remember here is that they shouldn't be a "sales pitch." They should be written in a way that offers solid advice or information to the reader. For instance, you wouldn't write an article about the whitening services you provide; but you may write an informative piece on the dangers of teeth whitening (especially home kits) or the pros and cons of teeth whitening.

The key here is not to sell your practice, but to sell you by setting you up as the community expert that everyone turns to for answers.

The reader (and editor) should never be able to tell that it is a marketing tool, written by a copywriter who specializes in marketing copy, but rather, an unbiased account written by a professional journalist. This can be done in several ways: by offering expert advice or by offering a unique how-to approach to the subject.

The Expert Says ...
In "the expert says ..." type of article, the writer will use your knowledge to tackle a subject. This can be done on a one-time basis or even a regular column. Since it may be difficult to convince an editor to give you your own column right away, many doctors prefer to pay for editorial "ad" space for the first few months until they've established a readership.

The How — To Article
Although the how-to piece still refers to the expert being shown, it is written in a very consumer-friendly how-to manner. For instance, you may offer "10 Tips to A Whiter Smile," or "5 Things to Avoid in the Dentist's Chair." Just be sure that you are giving them solid information they can really use.

When writing either of these types of marketing articles there are a few things to keep in mind:

Finding The Right Angle
Find an angle that will both hook your reader and give them something they can relate to.

Don't Imitate A Salesman

The last thing you want to do is come off sounding like a salesman. That will get your article thrown in the trash. Instead, offer practical tips the reader can use, whether they become one of your patients or not.

Although this type of article or press release is generally used for print publications, it can also be sent to TV and radio producers with a letter that asks them to consider using you as an expert source for any segments they may run on dentistry.

Website Design

If there's one thing I want to stress about websites it is this: *Every dental practice needs one!* Yes, you heard right, I said EVERY dental practice. Now, before you argue that a small one-doctor practice doesn't need a website, let me explain why it is so vital improving your bottom line:

- Nearly 80% of all online users have used the Internet to research doctors and dentists in their area. That means that 8 out of every 10 people who may call to make an appointment won't, simply because they can not get the information they want – and need – off of your website. Why? Because you don't have one!

- The U.S. web market is growing by a whopping 2 million users every single month – and many of those people are using the Internet to find information about certain services and procedures. That means if Mary Jones, who lives on Main Street in your community needs to have a dental implant, the odds are good she will try and find information about it on the Internet – and that search may lead her to your website – and your dental practice! A well designed website can provide timely information about innovation and new procedures in order to generate public interest in you – and your practice.

- It gives people instant access to your contact information (your address, phone number, office hours, etc).

- A website provides support for your current patients.
- Now, here is one of the most important reasons why you need a website: most of the other dentists in your area already have one! So, if you don't, you're helping to drive your competition forward while you lag behind.
- A website gives you easy tracking capabilities to see what type of patients are logging on, what they are interested in learning more about (which can give you important insight into expansion opportunities), to meet those needs, and make more money.

Now that you better understand the need for a website, let's talk about how to make it work for you. Most dentists don't think that a website can affect their bottom line, but the fact remains, it can – and will – improve your bottom line and help to increase your productivity by moving patients through the office more quickly, allowing you to get more done in a single day, if, of course, you use this important tool properly.

TIP ...

One thing you want to be very careful of when designing a website is thinking of it as an electronic brochure. It is so much more than that. Too often, doctors limit what their website offers by failing to see its potential.

What Your Website Must Feature

Let's face it, there are a lot of things you *can* put on your website, but first let's look at the things you *must* include on your website. First and foremost is your contact information. Make sure that your name, address, telephone number, fax number and office hours are prominently displayed so they are easy to find.

Next, you'll want to offer a brief description of all of your services, highlighting those that you wish to expand. In addition, be sure to include information on the insurances you take (maybe by offering a question and answer section for those FAQ you don't want your staff to have to take the time to answer over the phone over and over again throughout the day), plus any payment plan options that you may offer.

In addition to these basics, be sure to include the following on your website:

- **Lots Of Pictures Of Yourself And Your Team.** This can go a long way to removing whatever barriers there might be for a patient before they ever step through your office door. Nothing reassures a patient more than seeing a picture of a happy, smiling, friendly dentist and staff. It helps to make them feel comfortable and confident before they even meet you!
- **A Before And After Treatment Gallery.** People want to know what they will look like when you are finished with them, and the best way to show them the results they are after is with a "before and after" gallery on your website. This lets them take their time to look closely at your great work and see how a certain procedure can enhance their own smile. Now, if you're worried that it will be one of those cookie-cutter weak smile before and brilliant smile features that everyone has seen a thousands times before, don't. There are plenty of ways to make your site really stand out and look fresh and innovative. But we'll talk about that in a bit...
- **Emergency Contact Information**. Believe it or not a lot of people will go to the Internet in an emergency to see what to do next instead of calling. One reason may be because it seems less intrusive. Regardless of why they turn to the computer in a time of crisis, the fact remains that they do, and you need to highlight your emergency procedures and contact numbers on your website.
- **An Online Store For Products**. Many dentists are now offering online ordering options on their websites for products they keep in stock in their office such as whitening kits, mouthwash, specialty toothpastes, and more.

- **Feedback Surveys**. Want to find out what your patients really think about your office and your staff? Offer an online patient survey. They'll love the chance to give you feedback in the privacy of their own home (instead of having a receptionist staring at them while they fill it out) and it will give you the opportunity to learn what you are doing right (or wrong). Plus, you can pull blurbs and quotes form the surveys you like and add them to your patient testimonial page.
- **Patient Testimonials**. Speaking of patient testimonials, it's always important to let current and prospective patients see how many former patients have liked your office – and your great dental work! This can include quotes, letters, and in some cases, even before and after pictures of patients (if they agree).
- **Online Newsletters And Blogs.** A great way to draw people to your site is to offer the opportunity to congregate and talk about dentistry. People love to communicate via the Internet these days. You may be surprised at how many people visit your website when you attach a blog to it. Besides, it is a great way to find out what dental procedures interest people most, plus it gives you the opportunity to speak as an expert on those topics.
- **A Visual Office Tour.** This is a fantastic way to make new patients feel more comfortable since it makes them feel as if they've already been in your office as soon as they enter the reception area. A recent survey estimated that 50% of people get nervous just thinking about going to the dentist, especially a new dentist. So, adding a virtual tour to your website can help alleviate their stress and make them much more relaxed for their visit.
- **Kid's Corner.** You don't have to specialize in pediatric dentistry to give your younger patients something to do on your website. Just add some printable coloring pages, games or fun cartoons. Kids will love it and so will their parents since parents are always looking for safe websites for

their kids to visit. One doctor reported buying a few fun video games from a company for his website only to discover dozens of new patients calling to make appointments soon afterward. He was amazed to discover that one of his young patients had gotten every kid in his fourth grade class hooked on the games, and the parents were so impressed with the doctor's website that many became patients. Investing a few dollars in some video games resulted in several families joining the practice and bringing in more than $40,000 in extra revenue that year!

- **Coupons And/Or Discounts.** This can be a good way to entice new patients into the office or even convince a current patient to try a new service (such as teeth whitening). Other benefits to using online coupons: they are basically free (no printing, mailing or advertising fees) and they are easy to track to see which ones are the most effective.
- **FAQ.** Most people have lots of questions about dentistry, but may be too intimidated to ask you in person. Use your website as a way to educate them in both basic dental procedures and the more complicated ones you offer.
- **Patient Forms.** A huge timesaver for your office staff (allowing you to get through more patients in a typical day), putting all of your patient forms (insurance, health surveys, new patient forms, etc), online will allow all of your patients to fill them out before coming into the office and even submit them online if you'd like.

While this may seem like quite a list at first glance, it really is just a sampling of the many, many things that your website can offer.

Now, let's talk about one of the main benefits virtually every dentist can count on if they design a great website: a reduction in overhead costs. You may be asking yourself, "How is going online going to help me reduce my costs?" The first is by reducing phone traffic at your front desk. With more than two-thirds of patients more than likely to click on the computer for directions, appointment times, etc., rather than pick up the phone, some larger offices may actually be able to reduce phone and front desk help once their clients get used to their Internet capabilities. Or, if you don't want to get rid of any staff members, you can put them to work on more important tasks, thus increasing your productivity even more!

Some other benefits you may not have thought of that an office website may offer include:
- The ability to link your website with your patient scheduling software. This will allow patients to request appointments online. Of course your computer will have the ultimate control over what appointments are made, but it can be a real time saver for both front desk staff and patients alike.
- The ability to offer post treatment instructions. It is a lot easier to refer patients to the website for post-op instructions on more basic care than to have someone sit with them and explain it, then photocopy a sheet outlining what you've already told them. Besides, people forget what you have said almost immediately upon leaving the office, so having these instructions online can be a big help to ensure that they follow your instructions once they get home.

With so many ways to utilize a website, it's amazing to think about how many dentists simply disregard this wonderful opportunity to reach more patients and stay in touch with current (and former) ones. Once you begin to really use your website, you will begin to make it a central part of your marketing plan and practice by giving your patients exactly what they want and need: an easy place to get their questions answered; a place to make quick appointments; a place for their kids to go online without risk; and more ... much more.

What A Website Cannot Do For You

Now, we've been making it sound really good to have an office website – and it is. Obviously, there are some things a website cannot do for you.

The first thing is to understand that if you don't market yourself well, and begin to position yourself in the community using the other methods we have been talking about, a website isn't going to help you much. A website is only as good as you are willing to make it. It can take a bit of vision, creativity and forward thinking to make it something that will jump out and grab people. If you aren't creative and don't have a strong marketing sense, than the chances are your website will not have one either. That is why it is so important to hire the right people to design and maintain your website. Otherwise it will turn into just one more thing you have to take care of, with little – if any – real benefit.

Second, if you don't let people know you actually have a website, no one will use it. Sounds simple enough, yet most dentists never really make their website known to patients, or their community. Be sure that every piece of paper that leaves your office or marketing piece that touts your services prominently features your website address. That includes all advertising, brochures, postcards, letters, bills, appointment cards/reminders and more. Nothing should leave your office that does not include your website address somewhere on it. The more you put your name out there, the more traffic your website will get, and eventually word of mouth will take over.

What Is A Good Website?

One of the toughest questions we can answer in this section is, *"What is a good website and how do I define what a great website is?"*

There are a lot of things that can make a website stand out among the rest. Here are a few important points to consider when designing a new website or upgrading the one that you already use:

- **Make Sure That It Is Easily And Quickly Identified**. You want to make sure that people know who you are the minute they look at your website. Make sure that they can find what they need in just a few seconds, or you risk them clicking off and turning to another website – and doctor! Believe it or not, statistics show that most people take less than 2 seconds to determine whether or not you have a useful website or not. That's not a lot of time to WOW! them.
- **Make Sure That It Is Interactive.** Your website should allow your patients to do several things on it. People are very techno-savvy these days and they love to click on photos, focus down on a website to get more information, play video clips, in other words, they like to *play* on a website. If you don't offer a variety of things to do and see on your website, chances are the people who click onto it won't stay very long.
- **Make Sure That Your Website Is Up-To-Date.** Here's the #1 rule of websites: *never (and I mean never) put dated material on your website – especially if you don't intend to change it regularly.* It is usually best to only include items without a date or time stamp to ensure that isn't left posted for far too long, thus telling every visitor that you aren't paying much attention to your website. And, if you aren't paying attention to it, why should they?
- **Make Sure That Your Website Offers Clean And Intuitive Navigation.** What, you may be asking. What this means is that the buttons are arranged logically, and everything is labeled clearly. Make sure that specific pieces of information can be quickly identified and accessed to make the website as user friendly as possible. You want to make sure that every

button makes sense; otherwise users will become frustrated and leave.

- **Offer Multiple Ways To Connect With Patients.** Your website should offer several different ways to capture patient information and let them communicate with you. For instance, allowing patients to ask questions through an "Ask the Doctor" feature can be a wonderful way to connect with prospective patients. Giving a way to sign up for emails and newsletters can help you generate a good mailing list and gather the names and addresses of people who may be interested in your services in the future.

- **Make Sure Your Site Looks Different.** What do you think the most common color for a dental website is? Almost 90% are blue. Now, blue is a nice color for a website, but if your website is blue, that means it looks like 90% of all of the other dentists' websites out there and isn't grabbing the attention that you need. Be careful not to use the same color schemes, stock photos and articles that every other dentist in the region is using. Make sure your website stands out – make it look different!

- **Make Your Website Inviting And Comforting**. Dentists often elicit feelings of fear and anxiousness. People simply don't like going to the dentist, so anything you can do to ease their anxiety can only benefit you. Your website can be used as a tool to do just that. Be sure it includes a variety of soothing images (smiling doctor and staff and happy patients). Use a soothing color scheme. Forget the tight shots of lips and teeth. Nothing turns a patient off quicker than a huge picture of big teeth looking like they're about to jump off the screen at them. Instead, opt for casual pictures of happy children playing in the exam room or patients sitting quietly with the doctor and discussing a procedure. People are looking for an experience, just as much as they are looking for a procedure, so be sure that your website shows them how satisfying their next dental experience can really be.

Mistakes Dentists Make In Designing Their Websites:

As you have learned, there are plenty of things that a dentist can do to make their website more interesting and appealing. But, what types of mistakes are commonly being made? Here are a few to avoid:

- **Designing A Website To Impress Other Dentists.** Who cares what the other dentists in your area think of your website, as long as it is accomplishing the job you want it to.
- **Making Your Home Page Too Crowded.** The home page (or first page) of your website is where patients begin their website tour. Make sure that it isn't too loaded, or you risk turning them off before they have had a chance to see what you offer.
- **Sites That Takes Too Long To Download.** We're an instant gratification society, and if your website takes too long to come up on the screen, the odds are the person behind the computer will click off.
- **Including Flash On Your Website.** Flash can be a wonderful Internet tool, allowing websites to include movable graphics and other multi-media presentations. Unfortunately, it is not good for dental websites. Why? For several reasons:
  a. It takes to long to load
  b. It may require an additional download to read
  c. If you go back and forth through different sections of the website, you may have to reload the flash several times
  d. It can be over stimulation and hard to use

Good for some services and businesses, flash is not good on dental websites.

- **Using Bright Reds (the color of blood).** Anything that reminds a patient of blood (any bright red object on your website) is going to be a negative aspect. That doesn't mean you can't use limited amounts of a nice burgundy, but avoid anything that may give off the appearance of blood.

- **Too Much Text.** People hate to see all text and no graphics. Sure, they want information, but only in small digestible chunks. They are not interested in learning every facet of a procedure, just the basic facts. This can be done easily with small tidbits, bullets and lists.
- **Adding Too Many Links To Other Sites.** It's generally okay to add a few links to sites which can offer more in-depth information on a topic, but refrain from adding too many. The goal here is not to send your guests off to another site, but to keep them on yours.
- **Adding Too Many Credentials.** It sounds crazy, but few patients really care how many organizations you belong to or what awards you have won. All they really care about is that you can do the job. Be leery of adding to many credentials to your website, lest your patients think you are bragging.
- **Adding Counters.** Counters are updated and misleading, plus they can have a negative outcome. What if a patient thinks your counter should have a 100 and it only reads 25. Maybe you've recently reset the counter, but they don't know, or care. All they know is that no one is clicking onto your website and they're wondering why.
- **Domain Names That Are Too Long.** Keep it short and easy to remember

As you can see, developing a solid marketing plan isn't difficult, but it does require a little time, energy and know-how. While it is possible to handle these new strategies in-house, most dentists ultimately decide to hire a public relations or marketing guru to at least develop their initial plan of action and begin implementing it. Once your plan is underway, many of these ideas can then be handed over to others in your office to sustain.

Need some help with your website? I suggest you contact DentalWebsites.com. You can contact them at 888-906-1667.

Chapter Four:

Increasing Your Profitability

We've all heard the old adage: work smarter, not harder. But how will that apply to your dental practice? Wherever you are in your career, you should be interested in growing your practice, but that shouldn't mean that you are working long hours and adding weekend appointments to your already busy schedule. There are many ways to increase production and you may be surprised to find out what a difference that increase will make to the bottom line of your business.

What if we told you that with a 20% increase in production, you would actually be realizing a 54% net profit increase? Sound too good to be true? Well, this time it's not. Let's take an example and see how that would work out with some real numbers. The average dental practice runs 4 days per week, with 8 patients per day. Take that to the average of 48 weeks per year and figure the income to be about $2,000 per day, just for the doctor, not the hygiene patients. We're up to about $384,000 per year, minus the 65% overhead (which we will talk about lowering in a later chapter) and you have a profit of about $700 per day and $134,000 per year. That is a snapshot of the average general practitioner in America.

Let's boost the production of our Dr. Average by just 20% and see what happens. That accounts for $300 per hour, $24,000 per day and $460,800 for the year! The overhead doesn't increase, but let's take out a little bit for additional supplies or incidentals and we come up with a new net profit of $206,592 – that's quite a raise for our average doctor! Without working extra hours or adding overhead costs, our neighborhood dentist just gave himself a $70,000 raise. Let's see how he managed to get that increase.

We are going to discuss the ten keys to increasing productivity in this chapter, and how to implement them into your own practice so that you can reap the rewards of that 20% (or more!) increase in productivity and see the benefits at the end of the year when your profits have soared.

#1: Make 20% Your Goal

Understanding your practice and its profit margin is the first step to increasing productivity. If you need to sharpen up your hygiene department or work harder with your front desk staff to keep your broken appointment rate down, then do it today. Keeping all appointments on time will help you maximize the number of patients you can see in one day and if your hygienists are also running on time, your office will be humming with productivity. Like any other goal, you should claim the goal of reaching a 20% increase and be on the lookout for large and small ways to meet it.

Once you realize that just a small increase in your practice's overall productivity can have such a large impact on your profitability, you will be very motivated to look into new technologies such as digital x-rays or IV sedation, which we will look at a little more in-depth later.

#2 Quadrant Dentistry

Most dentists in America are doing single tooth dentistry and it's a shame. Once you have a patient in the chair, it is much more cost effective to work on more than one tooth in the quadrant when the patient is numb and ready to have one tooth filled or other work completed. In the same appointment and with the same overhead cost, you could be doing work worth three to four times as much as a single tooth procedure. Dr. Roy Smith, a multi-million dollar a year dentist in a small Texas town has grown his business on the concept of quadrant dentistry.

He uses compassion and understanding to build trust with all of his patients and gives them advice on what procedures may be in their future. In a true soft sell, Dr. Smith is able to explain the benefits of quadrant dentistry to his patients, which go well beyond the profit for himself. For the patient, quadrant dentistry is less time consuming and will require less time away from work or family obligations.

It is also a great way to make sure that all of your dental procedures "match." This means that the shades of crowns or veneers done at the same time will have a more natural look than those done months or even years apart. Dr. Smith also feels that by having a patient take care of a larger amount of work in one visit, you are ensuring that they will have the work done and won't come back after a few months needing emergency care on something that was left undone.

Of course, if the patient isn't interested in having quadrant work done, or if they can't afford it, then that is their prerogative. As their caregiver, it is up to you to listen to the needs and desires of your patients above all else.

#3: Get Paid Up Front

Dr. Smith shared with us that he learned his lesson early on in his practice not to finance out of his own office. After writing off nearly a quarter of a million dollars in unpaid bills, he made sure he wouldn't be in the same predicament again. While most patients have every intention of paying, they may be unable to do so after having the work done. Dr. Smith relies on his office staff to settle billing terms before any procedures are done.

Costs are discussed up front and payment arrangements are made before the work begins. His practice provides third party financing for patients, which is easily affordable and works on the MMP plan: Minimum Monthly Payment. We suggest that you have this type of financing readily available for patients and even that you have a breakdown of costs versus payments ready for them to see just what their treatment will cost.

When you have an informed patient and guaranteed payment, you have the best of both worlds. Your patient feels comfortable moving forward with treatment because he knows exactly how much it is going to cost and how he is going to pay for it, and you have the security of knowing that the financing is in place and you won't be out that money somewhere down the road.

#4: Have An Emergency Plan

This one doesn't relate to your fire drill strategy, it's about the way you handle emergency patients. Most of us see the emergency patient as a nuisance, sad, but true. We hope that each day will run according to schedule, especially when we are trying to concentrate on boosting production and increasing our profit margin.

Adding an uncomfortable and possibly brand new emergency patient to that mix doesn't seem like a recipe for success, but if we use Dr. Smith as an example, we can see that he is able to incorporate the emergency patient into his practice as an additional income source by using his associate to take care of him/her. He is able to maintain his appointments and because he has a protocol plan in place for his associate to follow, he/she knows just what to do to put the emergency patient out of pain and get him/her started on a treatment plan.

Let's see what he said, after meeting with his new associate and determining his/her skill and comfort level with certain treatments:
"Last Thursday morning we met and he/she doesn't do molar root canals. So I said, Jim/Julia (his associate) what you need to do is if somebody has a broken tooth and I'm not here and you don't want to do the root canal and crown, let my staff go in there and sell it for you and then just do a pulpotomy or go halfway down the canals and do your pin build-up and take your impression for the crown so you've got a couple of thousand dollars on the books."

Dr. Smith knows that if he didn't have a treatment protocol in place with his associate, he/she would have given the emergency patient an antibiotic, some pain meds and a bitewing, all for $49 and it would be likely that he/she would never be back in the office again. Because of their good communication and planning, they have given the patient a head start on reconstruction of his/her tooth and made a much larger profit than they would have if they hadn't been so prepared.

#5: Delegation
This can be a tough one for many of us. If you are a dentist in a solo practice, you are not accustomed to depending on others for much, if anything.   But, as regulations have changed allowing assistants and hygienists to take on larger and more important roles in the dental office, we must also change and allow them to use their skills to the best of their potential. The more we can delegate, the more patients we will be seeing and the more complex procedures we will be able to concentrate on.

If you have taken on even a part time associate, you will soon see the benefits of delegating.   You will still be producing the vast majority of your practice's income, but your associate can take over your hygiene checks, freeing you up to handle more patients or to offer longer appointments and concentrate on the all important quadrant dentistry we were discussing earlier.

Delegating work to your staff also builds employee morale as your staff will see your confidence in their abilities and will want to live up to your high standards. No one wants to work for someone who thinks they have to do it all; everyone wants to be valued for their particular contribution to the team.

#6: Combining Procedures
Just as we learned about quadrant dentistry, combining procedures cuts down on the amount of visits a patient needs to schedule and increases the profit margin for you exponentially. Dr. Smith is an expert at this, often doing crown prep at the same time as an endo appointment. He will take the impression and then finish the root canal when he is ready to seat the crown. It's a simple concept, but one that many dentists are reluctant to embrace.

For the patient that is afraid or anxious to be in the chair, combining procedures is a great advancement in care. They will only have two appointments to keep rather than three or four to have the same amount of work done.

For you and your staff, the combination of procedures is a goldmine. You can book one operatory, get the patient ready, check hygiene in another while your assistant is taking an impression. Even check on another patient who is getting numb, all while working a longer procedure on the first patient.

#7: Six Procedures You Should Be Doing
You may not realize it, but the least income producing procedure you are performing is simple fillings. They have the lowest income of any type of treatment you are giving at your practice. One of the things we stress to dentists who are struggling with increasing overhead and trying to boost production is to take a look at their procedure mix. That is the types of treatments you are offering and the amount of each procedure that you are performing. If you can incorporate the following six procedures into your practice, you will see a great increase in your production. To see how we use them in our practice, you can visit our website at www.plazadentalgp.com.

- Teeth whitening: It doesn't take a rocket scientist to figure out that people love to whiten their teeth. Celebrities and regular people alike are looking for that perfect smile and you can give it to your patients in your office and make a great profit while doing it. There are several types of whitening: basic tray whitening, Zoom whitening and the deep bleaching technique by Dr. Rod Kurthy. Whatever types of whitening you choose to offer, the net income is great and your hygienists or assistants can provide the service, you just have to make sure you have the space to accommodate the whitening client. If your staff needs to be trained to perform any of the whitening techniques, you should consider that a worthwhile investment because the satisfaction of your clients will be your best advertisement for the procedure. The investment will more than pay for itself in a short amount of time.

- Interceptive orthodontics: You don't have to be an orthodontist to provide this type of orthodontic care to your patients. And the Occluso-Guide™ is a relatively new device developed by Dr. Earl Bergerson to reshape overbites, overjet, crowding or spacing by using orthopedic action to move the teeth into near perfect occlusal. If you choose Invisalign™ as your practice's orthodontic device, you will need additional training, but you are also reaching out to a different demographic than you would be reaching with your general practice and you will see your profits increase.

- Cosmetic Dentures: Dentures that are so realistic they can even fool the spouse of the wearer! This three-step process is so simple and is a great asset to your patients who may have been hesitant to opt for dentures because they look so unnatural. Again, you are stepping out of your comfort zone, but into an area that has the ability to be extremely profitable.

- Silent Night: You can cure your patients' snoring in your office! That will be music to the ears of many of your clients and even more to their spouses. While many snoring and sleep apnea sufferers have a C-pap machine that they sleep with to help them breathe easier at night, these devices are cumbersome, tedious to clean and is difficult to take with you when you are on vacation or traveling on business. The Silent Night device looks like a traditional retainer, but it pushes the lower jaw into a position that essentially opens the airway of the wearer, allowing better breathing and eliminating snoring. This device is in extremely high demand right now and would be a great addition to your practice.

- Snap on Smiles™: Just as the name promises, this is a quick fix for tons of dental problems and will give the appearance of a healthy and straight, beautiful smile at an affordable price and in just a

week's time. The appliance is specially made for each patient and can be worn while eating and drinking. While it is not a long-term solution for dental problems, it can help with immediate appearance issues and it is very affordable for the patient and low cost for the practitioner.
- Bad breath treatment: Who better than you, the dentist, to treat your patients' breath issues. They already trust you with their oral care and now you can offer them another option for problems with their breath.

By adding these treatments into your procedural mix, you will be maximizing your profitability and remember what we started with? Just a 20% increase in production would be enough to realize a 54% increase in net gains.

Imagine if you could book a whitening appointment every day, or just a few anti-snoring appliances a week. Just the Snap on Smiles™ will bring in a $1,500 fee with only about a $200 lab fee-charges... that could really add up to big results for you. Your patients will be thrilled that the dentist they already rely on and trust is able to provide them with even more services than ever.

#8: Technology

We are all easily dazzled in this technology age; from wide screen TVs to iPhones, we seem to want it all and want the newest and best of everything. When you are considering a technology for your dental practice, you should always keep an eye on the bottom line and take the time to investigate the technology, the relative cost and what the new technology will bring to your practice.

One of the biggest technological advances that is making its way into the dental office is filmless x-ray machines. If you have a busy hygiene department and you make the investment in a laptop system that can move from operatory to operatory, the technology could pay for itself in as little as a few months. You will see an almost immediate increase in production of at least 20% just from making the switch to digital x-rays. Your hygienists will work more efficiently, which will in turn free up more of their time and the trickle down effect will increase your production as well.

When it comes to technology, there is also something to be said for impressing your patients. Today's patient is informed about their dental care, possibly even used the internet to search for just the type of cutting edge dentist they were looking for.

You have to achieve that balance between keeping up with technology and getting in over your head financially. The Cerec is a perfect example. An expensive machine such as this is not suited for a smaller practice. In order to recoup the expense of this type of technology, your office would need to be doing a couple of hundred crowns per month. It is tempting to want all the new gadgets and we all fall prey to that occasionally, but learn to grow the business first with technology that you can afford and then, when the timing is right, you will be able to upgrade to the big stuff!

#9: Procedural Flowcharts
Dr. John Lyons has created flowcharts for every possible dental procedure. Some practitioners love them and others hate them, but we all have to recognize that following a flowchart and sticking to procedural standards will increase efficiency, even down to the use of instruments. If you are doing crown preps and following one of Dr. Lyons' flowcharts, you will have only a limited number of instruments on the tray. If you have 10, you will likely use all 10; if you have 3, you will be able to complete the procedure with just the 3 you are allotted.

#10 Strategic Treatment Planning
Part of building that trust relationship with your patient is having a plan in place to address all of their needs and give them an idea of how you are going to treat them. Especially for the anxious patient, the treatment plan is a guide for them to understand how much work is involved

and what type of time and financial commitment will be involved to have the work done.

As the doctor, it is vital that you become a strategist, working in a logical and methodical way to get all of the work done on each patient in the most efficient way. This will likely lead back to the concept of quadrant dentistry, especially in the patient who needs extensive work completed. The more you practice strategic planning, the fewer appointments you will need to complete even complex work on a patient. If you can do the same amount of work in fewer appointments, you are doing yourself and your patient a great service. They will miss less work and spend less time in your office and you will make exponentially more profit from each appointment.

Intravenous Sedation Dentistry

One of the things that Dr. Smith shared with us was the success and increased profit that IV sedation has brought to his practice. Just by offering his patients this option, he took his 2 million dollar practice to a 3 million dollar practice. One of the main reasons for this jump in profit is that Dr. Smith is able to do more and more full mouth cases when a patient chooses IV sedation for their pain management, something he wouldn't have offered before he was able to also offer this type of sedation.

Laws differ from state to state regarding intravenous sedation techniques and your practice will likely need to employ a nurse or other medical personnel to start the IV lines for your patients and monitor their vital signs while they are under sedation. The training for use of IV sedation also varies depending on where you go. Dr. Smith shared with us that he was able to attend a seminar in New York that was a full week of training. Other facilities offered much longer courses, but as a busy dentist, he was much more interested in the condensed course so that he could quickly incorporate the new technique into his practice.

Just the addition of an additional pain management technique has made a huge impact on Dr. Smith's already thriving practice. Once he began the sedation dentistry, he took on an associate who is able to check hygiene patients and perform simpler procedures while he concentrates on one client with extensive damage. His clients really appreciate the option of the IV sedation and it has drawn in many new clients who had previously avoided having dental work done from fear of pain or just the experience of having the work completed. Dr. Smith is an excellent example of many of the tips we have given on how to boost productivity.

Implementing all ten of these keys to productivity would be nearly impossible, but even if you work only half of these ideas into your current practice, you will realize an increase in production of much more than 20%. Remember, the idea is to work smarter, not harder. Once you have built up a strong and vibrant practice, you should concentrate on other streams of income besides your own working hours so that you can enjoy the fruits of your labor.

Chapter Five:

Increasing Your Bottom Line By Controlling Overhead Costs

Your dental practice, while it does exist to help people, is also a business with operating costs, staff costs and technology costs. You have to worry about overhead just as much as the hair salon down the street or the pizza shop you order lunch from every week. While they have different costs than you do, you all share the same desire to lower costs and increase profits. Understanding where you are spending money and why will help you evaluate and possibly overhaul the way you run your practice and reap the benefits of increased profit in short order.

Overhead is basically every operating expense to run your practice: payroll, rent or mortgage on your property, supplies and laboratory or equipment costs. If you are just starting out in your dental practice, your costs may be very high, especially for supplies, equipment and rent. If you have been in practice for years or are running your dental business out of part of your home, your overhead may seem low, but in reality you might be able to reduce it even further and increase your profits.

Most people don't go into dentistry to become business owners, but unless you think of yourself as a businessperson and your practice as a business, you will run the risk of, at best, running a low profit practice and, at worst, losing your business completely. Really having an understanding of the true cost of the overhead in your practice is the first step to making changes and seeing the bottom line changes that will happen, so let's breakdown the areas of overhead.

One mistake that dentists often make when evaluating the overhead for their practice is to wait for the accountant's inventory of profit and loss statement to arrive at the end of the year. At that point, they find themselves shocked at the amount of money their practice has spent as well as at a loss of how to explain the costs. A better plan would be to create categories of expenditures for each month with a goal for income for each month and keep a careful eye on the bottom line each and every month. You could easily involve your staff in watching the pot so to speak, by posting the spending and income goals somewhere visible to everyone and making it in everyone's best interest to keep costs down. However you choose to keep track of expenses, it must be done more often than once a year to be able to understand and track where your money is going.

If you don't already have an idea what the operating costs are for your practice, now is as good a time as any to take that close look and find out exactly how much you are spending on your overhead costs. Remember to take into consideration all your expenses: payroll, rent or mortgage payments, taxes, supplies, payments on equipment purchases or rentals and any other fees or expenses associated with your practice.

You can easily set up a system for tracking expenses — there are many computer-based accounting systems that will do the work for you. You can give your employees incentives for keeping the smaller costs under control —after all, the little expenses can add up to big bucks in the course of a year.

If you have a family member in your employ, or even several, you may not be paying them in a traditional way. You should count their salary at a fair market value along with all your other salaried employees to get a clear picture of your payroll. Similarly, if you own your property outright, you should still determine the fair market value of the property when calculating your operating costs. Using these values will give you a more accurate picture of your costs and your profits.

The average overhead for a dental practice is somewhere between 60 and 65%, meaning that for every dollar you bring in, you are only making a profit of 35 to 40 cents. While some practices may claim to run on 40% overhead, a more realistic goal would be somewhere in the 50-55% range.

Another factor will be to increase profits while not increasing the amount of work you are personally putting into the practice. If you can increase the income to your practice while lowering your overhead, it will truly be a win-win situation. So, reduction of overhead is only one piece of the puzzle, but it is an important one. Let's break down where your money is going.

Cost Analysis

As an independent dental practice, you may not realize what the averages are for overhead across the board. It's important to see where your money should be going on a monthly and yearly basis, so here is a breakdown of a practice with a good percentage of overage categories.

- **Salaries:** 20-25%: There is some variance in this area, but in general this percentage is a good goal for your practice.
- **Lab Fees:** 10%: Ideally, your lab fees will come in around 10%, a bit higher isn't unusual and will probably mean that your practice is performing higher-priced procedures.
- **Facilities:** 5%: That may be shocking and many practices are way above this amount for either rent or mortgage payments, but in order to be truly profitable, you should be striving for this amount. Also, if you are tempted to expand your office space or upgrade to a larger space, be sure to run the numbers and ensure that your ideas won't lead you to financial problems down the road. If your current space keeps your expenses down — stay there!
- **Supplies:** 4-5%: This category includes all your dental and other supplies. You may think this isn't too important, but as we will see later, just a small savings in a recurring supply bill can add up to big savings later on. Consider buying your supplies from a Buyer's Club like "The Profitable Dentist"

Buyer's Club at 800-683-4723 (through Darby Dental).

- **Miscellaneous:** 4-9%: Taxes, insurance premiums, telephone and other utilities are all grouped in this category along with marketing. The wide range accounts for the difference in the need for marketing dollars that we will address later.

Labor

Your employees, as you well know, are essential to the success of your dental practice. You, as a dentist, could not possibly run a one-person operation. Each employee serves a particular purpose and you would be hard-pressed to make do without a front office staff or a hygienist for even a few days. The success of your business depends on the efficiency and hard work of everyone who works there.

What you may not realize is that labor costs about 20 to 25 cents of every dollar your practice takes in. That's a big bite out of your potential profit, so let's take a closer look at where that money is being spent and what you can do to make the most of your staff.

For the purpose of determining overhead, you should calculate your own salary, basically your W-2 earnings, your contributions to retirement plans and any continuing education expenses that come out of the profit of your practice. If you have a full time associate, you should determine a salary for each of you with any additional income being calculated as entrepreneurial profit for the business.

The other major areas for payroll, as you know, are front desk, chair side assistants and hygiene. You can't run a million dollar dental practice with one person at the front desk and your hygienists are essential to increasing the amount of money coming into your practice, as we will see later. It is important to determine how much your staff payroll is costing your practice. A general estimate of payroll is about 25 to 30 percent of your total revenue.

Of course, this estimate will depend on your geographical area as well as other factors such as the length of service of your employees. You will have to pay a fair wage for your area, and if you are in high expense area, you will probably also be bringing in higher than average fees for your services so your percentages will be roughly the same.

If you have had a hygienist working for you for years, her salary may be as high as $85,000 plus bonuses. If you have a new graduate working for you, the cost will be significantly less. You will have to evaluate what you are paying your staff based on experience, average wages for your area and performance. Remember that if you can increase your income without significantly increasing staff costs, your percentage of payroll expenses will go down, even if you are paying out more bonuses to your employees.

It is hard to quantify the impact of your staff in monetary terms, but it must be done if you want to get a handle on your overhead and make your practice as profitable as possible. You value each member of your staff as an individual and for their personal contribution to your business, but you have to boil things down to a numbers game to see if you are really getting your money's worth or if you are overpaying your staff or overstaffing your office.

While it's not a foolproof formula, one way to determine the amount of staff you need is to simply equate one staff person with a monthly income of $20,000. If you have a monthly income of $80,000, then you should have four full time employees.

Wealth-Building Tip:
Dr. Earl Estep has given us a great rule of thumb for creating a profitable dental office. Do you know how much it costs to run your office for one day? Well, figure it out — take your yearly overhead and divide it by the number of days your office is open, that will give you the daily cost of operating your office. In order to be successful and

build wealth, you should be making $2,000 above whatever your daily cost of running the business is!

The Front Desk
The front desk is an essential part of your dental practice. They are the first impression for your business and they can really make or break your practice. If your receptionist keeps people on hold for ten minutes the first time they call, it will probably be the last time they call. Conversely, a friendly, efficient front desk staff can be a great asset to your business. They can greet patients, make appointments, answer the phone and perform other administrative duties, but how many people do you really need to properly staff your office?

It is a good idea to determine how many patients your office sees in a day and determine how many staff members it takes to handle that amount of patient flow. Here, you could learn what other industries already know-that some times of day are "peak" hours, while others are slow times. Consider employing some front desk staff on a part time basis to handle those heavy times, especially if you have an associate and your hours overlap.

Another way to keep staff costs down when you have hourly employees is to have them clock in and out. This may not be very popular at first, but you may be surprised to find that your employees are not really working the hours you think they are if you have been previously using an honor system. The clocking in will both eliminate lateness and accurately track the amount of hours your employees are working so that you can see if you need to add staff hours or make other changes.

Money Saving Tip: Fire Your Answering Service
Traditional answering services are becoming a thing of the past, replaced by simple voicemail systems that have a page feature built in. While you may want to keep your front desk answering the phone during business hours, you can switch to an automated system for those after-hours and emergency calls. Keeping a page line open for

emergencies is simple and doesn't have the monthly cost of an answering service.

Hygienists

The other major category under the labor heading is hygiene. Your hygienists may actually be seeing more patients in a day than you are as the dentist and if they are able to keep their appointments and stay on time, your hygiene department will be a lucrative one. The standard has been that a hygienist should bring in three times their salary in production, so if you are paying your hygienist $45,000 a year, she should be producing $135,000 in income over the course of a year. But is it that simple? What is also essential in your hygiene department is efficient use of time, a good mix of procedures and getting the fees for hygiene right every time.

When it comes to chairside help, whether its hygienists or assistants, you will be well served to remember that you often get what you pay for. You may think you are getting a relative bargain by hiring someone who will work for a low hourly wage, but she may be unable to perform some duties or be lacking in certain skills that are essential to the success of your office. Depending on the laws in your state, hygienists and assistants can perform different duties and allowing your chairside employees to use all of the skills they can will both alleviate some of your own workload and increase the overall productivity of your office.

If you have two assistants, you could decrease the amount of time two patients will take by allowing your assistants to make a temporary or perform other tasks that their skills and your regulations allow.

You could nearly double the amount of patients you can see by employing skilled, reliable help. Your hygiene checks will go smoother and your assistants will be working to their potential so that your job will be easier.

Keep in mind that increasing production is another way to lower your overhead percentage. While it isn't truly lowering the costs, the additional income generated by efficient and competent staff will easily offset the cost of their salaries.

Equipment, Facilities & Supplies
Now that we have discussed the ins and outs of staffing, we should turn to the hard goods of dentistry. Your overhead will include any money you spend on supplies, lab fees, your facility and your equipment. If you have been in practice for years, your equipment is probably paid for, so you will have only occasional repairs to worry about. If you are just getting started in your own practice, you are likely overwhelmed at the prospect of outfitting your operatories.

One great way to save money on equipment is to consider using refurbished equipment. Oftentimes, doctors can find equipment that has never actually been used, and some has been used for only a month or two from these distributors. You can find chairs, units, Adec equipment, lights and more. Your patients will never know that the equipment is pre-owned, but your profit and loss statements will show the difference!

And, don't worry about service. You can still get excellent repair service even when you don't buy your equipment from the local guys. Repair companies want to make money, too, and they aren't concerned about where you purchased the equipment, they just want your repair business.

Buying Tip: Check out your options in the pre-owned equipment market before you buy new. Just like that new car loses its value the minute you drive it off the lot, these gently used pieces of dental equipment are available at a fraction of the price of new stuff. Check out sites like www.buydentalequipment.com.

Think outside the box and save money!

Once you decide to take a close look at your expenditures, you will realize that no expense is sacred. It may even take a few months of you signing every check to realize where the money is going and to plug the leaks that are causing your practice to waste money. Magazine subscriptions, unnecessary advertising dollars, and even some of your dental supplies may be draining your business of potential profit. It's time to take careful stock of every expense!

Have you ever considered supplies such as your yellow stone, white stone and rapid set stone that are expensive from your dental supplier? What if we told you that you could purchase the same product from Home Depot or Lowes for 75% less than you are paying to your supplier? Surprised? Well, another piece of specialized equipment is your air compressor and you will probably also be surprised to find out that you can purchase a standard air compressor from your favorite builders' supply store and with a few adjustments, save money and keep your standard of care.

Lab fees can be staggering, and you definitely want to use a reputable lab to do all of your crown and bridgework, after all, your patients are counting on your quality of care. You can find a better price than some of the "vanity labs" offer without sacrificing quality.

Offsetting Your Overhead By Increasing Production

As we mentioned briefly earlier, one way to offset the cost of overhead is to increase the amount of money your practice is producing. This might not sound too enticing at first as you may be thinking that we are suggesting adding night or weekend hours to your schedule, but that's not what we have in mind. As an independent dentist, you pride yourself on being a one-man or one-woman show, but you may want to consider bringing in an associate to increase the overall production of your office. This can be done in several different ways:

The Specialist:
If you live in a small town, specialists may be in short supply and bringing in an orthodontist, a periodontist or pediatric dentist will draw in more patients and create a steady stream of income for your practice. By treating the specialist as an independent contractor, you can pay him or her a percentage of the money they produce and keep the rest as profit. You won't be putting in extra hours, but you will be making extra money.

The Non-Dental Associate
While you are running a dental practice, you might be surprised to find out that you can invite a practitioner of another specialty to come in and use your facility while you aren't using it. A podiatrist is a good example of a type of non-dental professional that would be able to utilize your office on off-days or hours and one that could even generate business for your dental practice.

The Two-Day Associate
While most experienced dentists will tell you that partnerships and associations can be fraught with difficulty, a part time associate may be just the thing to infuse your practice with a steady stream of income. You may find a recent graduate who is eager to get some experience or a new mother who wants to keep up with clinical practice but only wants to work a few days a week. If you are able to plug in that associate on your off hours, you will be able to increase the amount of revenue your office generates without overcrowding your office or overwhelming your staff.

If your facility has the room, you could even work similar hours, with the associate taking the shorter appointments and you handling the more complex cases that take more time. This wouldn't put any more strain on your office staff, but would increase profitability exponentially. If you are working a four-day week, and your staff would agree to work Friday, your associate could put in a full day on Friday. Of course, your associate would have to understand that this association is not leading to partnership, nor are you preparing him or her to take over your practice so that you can retire. You are simply maximizing the potential of your office so that you can increase the production and reduce the overhead on your business.

The "Extra" Operatory

If you have an operatory that is often vacant, you may be sitting on a gold mine and you don't even realize it. Oftentimes, extra space in the dental office becomes a repository for supplies and other junk rather than a source of revenue. Don't let your facility sit idle, make use of that operatory and increase your productivity. If the rule of thumb is true, that you need to bring in $400 per square foot of space to cover expenses of the facility, then you really can't afford to have any square footage that isn't making money! You may not think you need that extra room, but here are few scenarios that may prove you wrong:

The average practice runs 3 operatories, but actually has 4. Two are used by the doctor and one by a hygienist. You may feel, as many dentists do, that your hygienist does just fine with one room and you don't need that fourth room. If your hygienist has access to that fourth room, she can prep her next patient while she is waiting for the doctor check on the current patient, staying on time and reducing the perceived wait time for your patients.

You could also book additional services using your hygienist and that unused room. Whitening is hugely profitable and could be added onto her appointment if the room she is in isn't needed for the next patient. She will be thrilled to have the whitening done right away and your staff won't have to schedule her for another appointment.

Emergency patients are another concern for the dental practice and the extra operatory may be just what you need to treat this type of patient. If your associate happens to be working on that day, then he or she can handle the emergency with even less disruption to the day's schedule and without having to turn away a person who is in pain.

Even if you consider that your operatory may cost $30 a day to operate, if you can produce $200 a day in that room, you have more than covered the costs and are making headway into lowering overhead and increasing profits.

Nine Quick Tips To Reduce Overhead
- Get a time clock
- Sign your own checks
- Scrutinize all expenditures
- Shop around for deals on supplies
- Get a coded postage meter
- Buy refurbished whenever possible
- Get all fees and coding right every time
- Evaluate staffing
- Make the bottom line everyone's business

Remember that you are running a business-and you want it to be profitable!

You may have thought that overhead was a set of fixed expenses, over which you had little or no control. We hope that you have learned that not only do you have control over many factors that make up your overhead; you have a responsibility to understand them and fix the ones you can. By getting personally involved in the financial portrait of your dental practice, rather than leaving it up to the accountants, you can make a huge difference in the profitability of your business. You will see the payoff in small ways in the short term and in much larger ways in the long run.

Chapter Six:

Convert Calls into Cash:

The Steps To Turning Every Call Into An Appointment

Up until now we have talked a lot about ways to bring new (and old) patients into your office door. We have discussed the benefits of reaching out to previous patients; what type of advertising and marketing tactics work best; and even how to control your costs for a healthier bottom line. But have you considered how your appointment team may be handling this influx of new patient calls?

The fact is, you can incorporate all of the tips we have talked about so far and even spend thousands of dollars in specialized marketing tactics, but if your phone team fails to turn every prospect call into a booked appointment, you might as well be throwing all of that money (and your time) out the window.

In this chapter, we will discuss some of the most common mistakes the phone staff makes when speaking with prospective patients and how to help them do a better job to turn every opportunity into an appointment. But first, let's discuss one of the easiest and cheapest ways to grab those new patients without investing another penny and very little time or energy: having your phone lines open all day!

Now this may seem like a silly, inconsequential thing, but trust me when I say that *it isn't*! Think about all of the prime calling times when your staff is unavailable and your machine handles incoming calls and messages. I bet there is one time during the day when every dental office reading this book basically shuts down: lunchtime. Did you wince when I said that? Are you one of the thousands of offices that let the answering machine field calls during this all-important hour of the day? Now consider this: statistics show that having someone on hand to personally answer lunchtime phone calls can result in $2,000-$5,000 (or more) in additional revenue each and every month for the average small one-dentist practice. That can mean an increase of at least $100,000 in revenue this year for most of you reading this book without investing another dime!

The fact is, all of that marketing you've been doing is pointless if someone calls your office and can't get through. Reports show that most new patients will only call once, with only a fraction of them taking the time to leave a message. Add to that the fact that the vast majority of people make personal phone calls early in the morning, late in the afternoon and during their lunch break at work. Unfortunately, these are all times of the day when your office may be leaving the machine to handle incoming calls, and getting a machine when you have limited time to get your questions answered can turn a potential patient away from you and toward whatever dental office they can get a hold of.

"This is an important blind spot that many doctors are not aware of," stresses Jay Geier, president of the renowned Scheduling Institute. "And it's costing them thousands of dollars in lost revenue every year."

If you've gone to the trouble of sending out a reactivation postcard to past patients, or set up a detailed marketing plan to bring in new faces to your practice, it makes sense that you have someone on the line at all times between 8 am and 6 pm to answer their questions and schedule appointments. "Like it or not, most people hate voice mail and answering machines," stresses Geier. "And won't leave a message. Unfortunately, many of them will not call back. That's a missed opportunity."

It's amazing to think how so many offices are losing out on such a great opportunity; with something as simple as manning the phones during the entire day (even lunch breaks), resulting in dozens of new patients every month. "It isn't unusual," says Geier, for many doctors to balk at the idea, thinking it impossible, yet are surprised to discover its truth once they implement a new phone answering policy. Try it, you too may be surprised by the results!

Handling Appointment Calls Properly

Now that you understand the importance of having someone on hand to answer every call – no matter what time of the day – it's important that you evaluate how your staff is handling those calls. Statistics show that nearly 90% of dental offices fail to handle new patient inquiries properly, which results in lost opportunities. Unless your office strives for turning every call into a scheduled appointment, you are losing good patients and a lot of potential income!

Let's look at a few facts:
- The ADA estimates that every new patient results in a $2,000-$5,000 increase in revenue for the doctor
- More than half of new patients that call are looking for a dentist for their entire family, which can result in acquiring 2-4 new patients (that can mean more than $20,000 in increased revenues)
- If the office staff fails to set an appointment while the prospective patient is on the phone, the odds are slim the caller will ever call back
- Most of the mistakes office call handlers make include:
  a. Not being friendly enough
  b. Going into too much detail when answering questions (thus confusing callers)
  c. Requiring the caller to call their insurance company for payment information
  d. Playing verbal ping-pong (caller asks question; handler answers question)
  e. Not trying to "close the deal" by actually scheduling an appointment

Considering the fact that so few call handlers have actually been trained how to answer inquiry calls from new patients, its no wonder so many prospective patients are lost. According to Geier, whose Scheduling Institute evaluates how individual offices handle incoming calls and teaches the staff proper techniques to winning over new patients and turning every call into a scheduled appointment, there are only a few types of calls an office will receive and its up to the handler to figure out which type of call it is (and his/her response) within 5 seconds, or risk losing the patient.

Some of the most common calls a dental office receives include:
- Current patients with an emergency
- Current patients needing preventive care and/or maintenance
- Prospective patients who have been referred to your office by a satisfied client
- Prospective patients who are responding to some type of advertising or marketing tactic
- Prospective patients that are new to the area and have never heard of your practice before

How you handle each of these calls will be a bit different, however, there are some important things to keep in mind when speaking to any prospective patient for the first time:

Greet New Patients With Enthusiasm And Interest
Certainly it's important to appear genuine (not too salesy and fake), but every time one of your staff members picks up the telephone, they have to appear to care whether or not that caller actually comes in for an appointment. This can be hard for someone who must man the phones and basically answer the same exact questions all day, every day. However, callers don't think about that. All they hear is disinterest and that can be very offensive.

One way to help your staff find the enthusiasm and interest to deal with the 1,000th question on new patient appointments and insurance for the week, is to help them better understand what that call really means. It is more than someone looking for information, or even a new dentist. The ADA estimates that every new patient equals at least $2,000 in revenue – and every call is a potential new patient. That means that every time your staff answers a new patient call, they have the ability to raise your revenue by $2,000 – and usually much more.

Many doctors find that offering phone handlers a $5-$10 bonus for every new patient appointment that they make (and is kept) beyond a certain number every month increases the staff's willingness to try a few of the suggestions we'll be discussing. That means, for instance, if your office made 25 new patient appointments last month, your staff would get this minimal bonus for every appointment beyond that number next month; with the number rising the following month to accommodate the new appointments generated the month before.

Certainly, that means paying your staff a few extra dollars for doing the job they were hired for in the first place, but considering the fact that each appointment will likely generate hundreds, if not thousands of dollars in revenues, isn't it worth $5 to $10 bucks to make sure that your staff is eagerly on board with your new phone program?

One of the best ways to greet someone on the phone is to offer the doctor or practice's name, your name, and ask how you can help them. Something as simple as *"Thank you so much for calling Dr. Steven's office today, my name is Jenn, what can I do to help you?"* Is all that's really needed? Just make sure it is said in a friendly, outgoing and enthusiastic manner.

Learn How To Answer Their Questions Properly
It doesn't matter how friendly or experienced your staff is, if they haven't been taught how to answer patient inquires the right way, the odds are they are doing it wrong. The Scheduling Institute, who monitors phone handlers at thousands of dentists' offices nationwide, estimates that 90% of office staff mishandle the vast majority of new patient calls. This can be devastating to your bottom line. But, before you begin to reprimand your staff for their ineptitude, ask yourself this important question: *"Would I do any better?"* The answer is: probably not.

Before we begin to discuss the proper techniques to handling a new patient call, let's take a look at how most of you (and your staff) handle an average call:

Office: Dr. Steven's Office. This is Shelley, how may I help you? (tone is dry and sounding a bit bored)

Caller: Yes, I'm looking for a new dentist for my children and me. Could you tell me what an initial appointment involves?

Office: How old are your children?

Caller: 12 and 9

Office: Usually the very first time we do an exam we take a bitewing x-ray; 2 x-rays if they haven't had them in the last 6 months and then we do a cleaning and put fluoride on their teeth.

Caller: Okay

Office: Does that answer it?

Caller: Yes. Now, do you take most dental insurance?

Office: As a PPO provider you mean? We send insurance forms in for you. We are PPO providers for Blue Cross/Blue Shield. MetLife, Aetna, Amertus and Delta.

Caller: But I have Sigma

Office: OK, we are not a PPO provider for Sigma, so we send the form in for you and they'll generally pay most of the bill.

Caller: I see, so how much will I owe?

Office: There's usually less than a 10% difference between what the insurance will pay and what we charge. You can always call your provider and ask them exactly what the difference will be.

Caller: I guess I'll give them a call then.

Office: Okay.

Caller: Thanks

Office: You're welcome, goodbye.

On the surface, this call may not have sounded too bad. After all, the receptionist answered all of the caller's questions, but she made a few mistakes along the way:
- Her tone was a bit bored and routine. Granted, she probably fields dozens of these calls a week, but she still needs to make the caller feel as if she cares whether or not she joins the practice.
- She allows herself to get involved in a game of verbal ping-pong, where the caller asks a question, she answers it and waits for the next question. There is no attempt at transition to telling the caller about the doctor and the practice or even make an appointment.
- She requires the caller to do her own research regarding her insurance coverage. Plus she was a bit confusing with her answers. Most patients know little (if anything) about dental insurance and throwing out words like PPO, participating doctor, fee adjustments, etc. will not only confuse, but scare off a potential patient. A better strategy here would have been for the receptionist to offer to look up her coverage on the computer when she comes in for her appointment, assuring her in a positive way that it will likely cover all but a few dollars of the

appointment costs. Telling someone they may be responsible for 10% of an outstanding bill sounds a lot worse than saying that most patients pay less than $10 out-of-pocket for the first visit. Let's face it. Most people are willing to kick in a few extra bucks for an out-of-network doctor they feel comfortable with and can trust.

- The receptionist's biggest mistake: she never even asks the caller if she'd like to schedule an appointment. The odds are slim that caller will ever call back, let alone make an appointment. Your office has just lost $2,000- $6,000 (for the caller and her two children), on that call alone. Now, consider how many of those calls come into your office every week, every month, every year. See how important it is to teach your staff how to answer new patient inquiries properly? Here are a few tips to try in your office:

Take Control Of The Call – Guide It In The Direction You Want It To Go

One of the most damaging mistakes most call handlers make is not taking control of the conversation. They wait for the caller to ask questions, only to confuse and frustrate them with too much information and no real direction as to what to do next. In our sample call, the office receptionist never makes an attempt to direct the call by offering information on the doctor, his office hours, the types of specialty treatments offered, etc. Saying something as simple as, "O*h, you have a 9 and a 12 year old, they'll love Dr. Steven. He has four children himself and has recently remodeled two of our exam rooms to better meet the needs of his younger patients. He's added TV screens, Ipods so they can listen to music and even flavored exam gloves. Our biggest problem now is staving off requests by our adult patients who want those rooms.*" See how the receptionist steers the call in a positive way that will help convince the caller that this is the office for her and her children?

Instead of letting the caller ask all of the questions, your staff should feel free to ask some of their own and transition from a question-answer volley into a scheduling session.

Be Upbeat And Positive
Again, always be upbeat and positive, even when a caller has a concern. For instance, by reinforcing the doctor's ability to work with children and their special concerns and fears, the caller can relax in knowing that your office is a child-friendly one. In addition, answer every insurance question in a positive light. All-too-often, call handlers actually discourage prospective patients from making an appointment by making it seem as if they don't take their insurance or that the patient will incur an unexpected out-of-pocket expense. When, in reality, visiting an out-of-network doctor in most cases results in minimal expense for the patient. Instead of saying, we aren't PPO providers for that type of insurance, say something like, although we aren't in your insurance network, the odds are that you'll only owe about $4 or $5 for the exam. In most cases, the patient will agree to pay a bit on their own in order to see a doctor that they think really cares.

Don't Bombard The Caller With Too Much Information
It can be very easy to get bogged down trying to answer what the receptionist believes is a complicated insurance question, when all the caller really wants to know is if you take their insurance and what it'll cost them. Instead of going into details about what a PPO is and how to find an in-network provider, simply state whether or not you accept their insurance and what it means if you don't. Something like, "No we don't belong to Sigma's network, however, that only means that we'll have to fill out a few more forms for you and you'll likely be required to pay about $10 for the first visit. Now, when would you like to come in?"

Be Helpful – Offer To Find Out Their Insurance Information For Them

Most people know very little about their insurance and dread picking up the phone and making the calls necessary to find out all of the details. One of the best and easiest ways to ensure turning a prospect call into an appointment is to offer to do the legwork for them. Offer to look up their insurance information on your computer when they come in for their appointment and deal with issues then. True, a few (very few) patients may walk out on their appointment if they discover that they will be responsible for a large amount of the bill, but most won't. Why? For several reasons: most people assume they will have to pay something for treatment and will accept the terms of their insurance; besides the fact that by the time they walk through your doors you've already established some sort of relationship with them. They already like and trust you to a degree and are willing to at least try you out before walking away. Of course, there will always be a small number of patients who cancel their appointment, but having one or two open spots per month is well worth the dozens of other ones a good phone closer will generate.

Be Interested In Their Problem, Whether It Is Finding A New Dentist In An Area They Aren't Familiar With Or Treating An Ongoing Problem

Always show genuine concern to your patients, whether you know them or not. New patients, especially, need to feel as if someone in your office "cares" about their problems or concerns. This may be accomplished by simply asking how they like their new community, if they know about any special community events coming up and the like. For those who express a concern about dental fears or bad experiences, the time to reassure them about your practice's experience and expertise is a must.

Never Hang Up Without Offering To Schedule An Appointment

The call handler's main priority should always be to schedule an appointment. That means that they should be on the lookout for opportunities in the conversation to encourage the caller to schedule an appointment immediately. Using such simple phrases as: *"What day and time is good for you," "May I schedule your appointment now?" "I have Friday at 10 open, are you available to come in then?" "When would you like to come in?"* can all help seal the deal and get this new patient scheduled.

Transitioning To An Appointment
One of the hardest things for most phone handlers to learn how to do is to transition a call from the question/answer mode to the appointment close. A good transition requires looking for opportunities in the conversation that lend themselves to staving off the next questions in lieu of moving forward to the next step: actually committing to an appointment time. Some good ways to transition would be ask the caller if they would like to know anything about the doctor; where they heard about your office; when they are available to come in; etc. Be sure not to make them feel as if they're asking too many questions or you don't want to be bothered. Simply guide the conversation into a different direction.

Closing The Call
A call isn't officially "closed" until an appointment is entered into your system. True, a few calls (very few) may result in a missed opportunity, but generally speaking, your staff should consider it unacceptable not to end a new patient call without an appointment. This can be a hard change for many to make. After all, you've never asked your staff to work as salespeople before, and many may not be comfortable with the idea of trying to sell your services. But the fact remains; each person on your staff has been selling (or not selling) your services since they started. Every patient they come in contact with in your office looks to them for the guidance and confidence they need to return. So, the next time someone on your staff says, but we're not salesman," answer, "Sure you are. You sell my services every day!"

Capturing Data

The final aspect of handling new patient calls correctly is date capturing, something few phone handlers are good at. No one in your office should ever hang up the phone with a prospective patient without having gathered these basic bits of information:

- *The patient's name*
- *The number of people in their family looking for services*
- *Their address*
- *Telephone number*
- *Possible insurance information*
- *The types of services they require*
- *Who referred them/how did they hear about your office?*

Armed with this basic information, you can at least send the patient a thank you for calling postcard or newsletter in the event they do not make an appointment. Making contact a few times may be all that's necessary to reel in a hesitant prospect.

The most important thing for you and your staff to realize is that people don't take the time to make these inquiry calls if they are not ready to buy your services. Most people would prefer not to call the six dentists on their list, but to find one right away who can make their decision easy to make.

"These people are in a complete state of readiness," stresses Jay Geier of the Scheduling Institute. "They've already qualified themselves to a certain degree by finding your number and then taking the time to call. You're not trying to sell them something they aren't looking for. All that's left is handling the call in a way that closes the deal with a scheduled appointment."

How To Handle Staff Objections

Now that you know the right – and wrong – ways to handle new patient calls, it is your job to help your staff understand its importance. This will require more than telling them all the things they have been doing wrong. After all, it isn't their fault – you didn't know they were handling calls wrong either!

The best way to approach your staff is during a staff meeting where you explain that you have been learning some new phone techniques that you want everyone to learn. Tell them about everything we've mentioned here and why you think it's important to give this new strategy a try.

Many will balk at the idea that what they're doing is wrong. That's okay. Just be firm about your intentions and insist that everyone follow the plan. Next, turn your front desk people into marketing agents by offering some incentive for all new patient appointments made during this transition time. This will give them a reason to give these tips a good solid try.

Next, teach them how to handle calls by following these basics: being welcoming and friendly, answering questions, looking for cues to making a transition and creating an outcome (a booked appointment), all without lags in the conversation. This isn't going to be easy, but it can be done.

The odds are you have been making a lot of small changes in your office thus far, and this is just one of them. Your staff should be seeing the positive results of these changes and be more willing than ever to go along with your new plan. For many at this stage of your practice building, it begins to become a game as to who can book more new appointments and how you're going to find these new patients.

Now, with so many new patients filing through your doors, you may wonder how in the world you are ever going to be able to treat them all. This, dear doctor, is all in the scheduling. Now, let's learn how to get more work done in less amount of time.

Chapter Seven:

Scheduling For Success

If you find yourself busy, busy, busy, but not very productive, than this chapter is for you! All-too-often our offices run like marathon athletes without ever really reaching the finish line. That can be exhausting, frustrating, not to mention unprofitable.

So, how can you turn your days from quick heats into slower churning (and more enjoyable) workdays, and still increase productivity – and profitability? It's not as difficult as it may seem, if you implement the philosophy of Straight-6-Scheduling. Never heard of it, you say? You're about to …

What Is Straight-6-Scheduling?

First introduced by Dr. Rick Kushner back in the early 1980s, Straight-6-Scheduling basically means that your staff is required to work six straight hours without breaking for lunch. According to Dr. Kushner, it makes the entire office more productive. Now, if you're like me, you're probably saying to yourself right now, *"Is he kidding, my staff would kill me! Besides, how much work can you get out of them with that kind of schedule!"*

Believe me when I say I was skeptical too, until I considered what happens right before lunch in our office: About 30 minutes before lunch everybody starts talking about it and what they're going to have, where they're going to go, what's good, that sort of thing. This results in a sort of la-la land from about 11:30 to 12:00 where things really don't get done like they should. Then everybody goes out and has lunch, returning around 1:10 or 1:15 for the next patient. Chances are they're now talking about the new pizza parlor down the road, or how much they ate, etc. It might take them another half hour to get in sync. Sound familiar? Now, that lunch hour just turned into two solid hours of poor (or no) productivity. Amazing, isn't it! Something as simple as a lunch break has killed your staff's motivation and kept them from being as productive as they could (and should) be.

Now, before we get into the details of Straight-6-Scheduling, let me add this point of interest: most offices that try it, love it – and for good reason. It makes the workday go quicker; the staff doesn't feel as rushed throughout the day; and get this, it often increases revenue by 75-80% without doing anything else differently! Yes, I said up to 80% without adding services, working longer hours or even raising fees. The simple act of working six straight hours allows you to see more patients by utilizing your time better and therefore make more money. Ready to learn how it works? Good!

You're familiar with the typical day in a dentist's office: you roller skate from chair to chair; stressed because you have all of these tough cases and emergencies crammed in one after another for 8-10 hours every day. You (and everyone else on your staff) feel rushed and exhausted, trying to stay on schedule only to be forced to stay late – yet again. It's a crazy life and you know it. But there is relief in sight. With Straight-6-Scheduling you will be able to experience a more leisurely pace, seeing the hardest patients first and slowly downgrading the work (and stress) as your energy tapers off throughout the day; plus you'll be able to stay on schedule – all of the time – rarely more than a typical 6 hour day. Think about that: getting all of your work done (and increasing your revenue) in a 27-30 hour workweek!

Worried that this new schedule will mean giving your patients less time and attention? Don't be! With the Straight-6-Schedule you will actually have more time to spend with your patients. As we get into more details later in the chapter, you'll see how this works. Plus you'll have the time and scheduling space to see those new "emergency" patients.

All of this from giving up lunch? Well, not exactly. It all has to do with the scheduling. The appointment book is the most important thing in your office – and you thought it was you! Your productivity, your profitability, your quality and yes, even the happiness in your office all hinge on how well that appointment book is managed. And it's also where most of your problems lie.

One of the biggest mistakes an office can make is allowing the receptionist the 32 lines that fill the spaces in the book between 8 am and 5 pm without ever considering what the procedure is or how it will affect other rooms being handled at the same time. This causes chaos and stress.

The first step to implementing this new plan is to change your scheduling to 10-minute increments instead of 15. This in itself can save you a lot of time.

Next, be sure to mark off all holidays, vacations and other time off from your schedule at least a year in advance. Few dentists do this. As a matter of fact, most do the opposite. They fill the schedule and then decide that they need a vacation and make the staff start rearranging the schedule. This can be very demoralizing, plus it wastes a lot of time.

Also be aware of other trends during the year and plan accordingly. For example, during the summer you want to maybe work a few extra days to work in back to school check ups.

Next, you have to start thinking about what procedures will be done when. It's important to fill the maximum production time blocks first (we'll explain this in detail in a minute). Then, once the block is filled, once you have the solid production in each day, then you build the schedule around other, lighter duties. This requires guiding your patients to certain appointment times, ones that are best for you. This will likely seem awkward at first (and maybe even a bit difficult to implement), but usually works out fine once your staff and your patients get used to the new system.

Also, be sure that your reception staff considers a patient's lifestyle when making an appointment. Be sure to save those early mornings and after school slots for the right patients. For example, a retiree can likely come in during the "off" hours, so give them those appointments and save the "prime" ones for people who really need them. It makes everyone happy and scheduling easier.

Now, let's look at how the system really works. Think about how you and your staff come into the office each morning: you're really fired up, you're well rested and you're ready to have a really productive day. And the first patient that is scheduled is a denture adjustment. And say this person has been one of these difficult denture adjustments where you've seen them 4, 5, or 6 times and so that's the way you start your day.

Now here is the problem, how long is that adjustment going to take? Sometimes it takes 5 minutes, sometimes 10 minutes but what if it ends up taking a half hour? You've just started your day and you're already behind. Psychologically you're set for having a bad day – and it's only 8:30! Starting out with a bad experience ruins your entire day.

Now, what if you started your day with procedures that were productive? No more adjustments; no more deliverables; basically nothing too unpredictable. You'd soon discover that you are setting the stage for a good day, so by the time you reach those unpredictable cases, you are already in a good mood, have experienced some success throughout the day, are running on schedule; and are in the mindset to handle what lies ahead.

Now, how are you going to accomplish that? By implementing the Straight-6-Schedule like this: working 6 hours straight with the first 3 hours of the day blocked out for productive procedures only. Begin by taking a green highlight marker and drawing a block around the first 3 hours of every day on the schedule.

Now, instruct your staff to only put certain types of appointments in this block: major crown and bridge work, the start of a denture or partial denture, impressions, oral, and quadrant dentistry where you're doing 1/4 or _ of the mouth at a time.

So when you do that in the green block the only procedures allowed in that block of time are major crown and bridge, denture impressions, long oral surgery, root canals and quadrant dentistry. Now here is the key – in the doctor's operatory nothing is booked in the other operatory. So if the doctor is working 2 operatories, nothing is scheduled except for the one chair for the first 3 hours of the day.

So, what should the hygiene department be doing during this time? The same type of thing: scheduling their productive procedures in the first 3 hours of the day. So that might be a C-Reactive Protein patient, 4 quads of scaling and root planning, etc.

Hygiene checks are done when the doctor has time. This means if the doctor is prepping, you do a hygiene check while the impression material is in the mouth. Checks are now done at the convenience of the doctor – not the hygienist.

Let's review the ground rules: the first 3 hours of the day are spent doing major production procedures. This allows everyday to be productive – not just busy. By using this new scheduling, most doctors find that they are just as productive in the first 3 hours of the day as they may have been in the entire day prior to using the system.

Now comes the next two hours (which you'll block out using a pink marker), which we call barbershop dentistry filled with the kind of intermediate procedures that are usually predictable. They go on time and this is where we would do consults, fillings, minor oral surgery, single crowns and we would do simple root canals.

During this two-hour time span, you will begin using your second operatory. This will allow you to prep a quadrant of fillings and an expanded duty dental assistant can come in and place those fillings while you're in the next operatory prepping another quadrant. While you will be going back and forth between rooms, you shouldn't be chair hopping to the same extent as you were before.

Finally comes the end of the day (which we'll block off orange in the appointment book), where your schedulers fill the spots with unpredictable cases such as deliveries, post ops, appliance checks and adjustments. Now, it may sound a bit crazy to put your most unpredictable procedures (and patients) in at the end of the day when everyone is tired and eager to get home. But consider this: you've already had 5 hours of pretty good work and you know that as soon as you get through this tougher hour you are done for the day. Makes sitting through a few rough ones a bit easier to manage doesn't it?

The other benefit of doing these types of procedures at the end of the day is that if something takes a little longer, it doesn't throw off your entire day and every appointment after it. You may get out 10-15 minutes later than normal, but honestly, that isn't as big a deal as it once was. Besides, to be honest, that doesn't happen often with this type of schedule.

Here's a rundown of your new 6-hour day: you run one room in the first three hours to handle major procedures, followed by barbershop dentistry in the next two where you run two rooms doing regular work, ending the day with an hour of unpredictable cases like deliveries, post ops, appliance checks, and adjustments.

Now, in order to make this schedule work, you will have to take some responsibility to let the front desk know where any follow-ups belong. This requires keeping a laminated copy of the colored blocks in each operatory for referral. When a diagnosis is made, a highlight mark is made on the chart to let the front desk know in which blocking to schedule that next appointment. For example, if a 3-unit bridge is needed, the chart will be marked green. This tells the receptionist that the next appointment goes in the green block. If it's highlighted in pink, she knows that it goes in that second block of time and if it's highlighted in orange she knows it goes at the end of the day. This makes it easy for the front and back office to communicate.

Now, one of your hardest sells for this new program will likely be your staff, so be prepared. Most of your staff will likely think you are crazy when you tell them what you plan to do. All they'll see at first is the fact that they'll be working 6 straight hours with no real break. Considering how hectic their days are right now, that's enough to scare them to death. That's why it is so important to keep reinforcing the fact that this new scheduling procedure is designed to take the chaos and craziness out of your days, allow you all to be more productive, and get more done in less amount of time.

Begin your sell by telling your staff that you learned about this new scheduling system and that you would like to try it just one day per week for a month or so. This will give them an opportunity to "try it out." Reassure them that if it doesn't work out, you'll be happy to go back to the old way of doing things. But they have to be willing to give it an honest try.

Another great tip offered by one dentist was to encourage the front desk to keep the schedule "clean" (not including any procedure that didn't match the color code for that time slot) by putting a dollar bill in a jar every time the doctor found a scheduling block "clean." At the end of the month the scheduling staff is allowed to split the money jar. This is a wonderful way to entice your staff to follow the new rules.

Next, pick a day in a few weeks (maybe a Tuesday) and instruct the front desk to schedule it according to the Straight 6 outline. After the first day, ask if they'd like to try another? Believe me when I say it only takes one or two days scheduled like this to get everyone asking for more. No one understands how it can change the entire way your office runs until you actually try it.

Once you try it I'll bet you never go back to your old way of scheduling.

Now, this does always elicit one important question: what to do about salaries. Let's say that you have a dental assistant who is making $10 an hour working 40 hours a week now, she'll only be making $300 a week under the new system (since she'll be working less) – or will she? You may think that this is a great opportunity to cut costs. Resist that urge! After all, most of you will increase your productivity under this new plan (and your profits), so why pay your employees less? I suggest keeping their salaries the same, despite fewer work hours. Thousands of doctors have tried this plan and none have reported losing money on the deal. Besides, who in your office is going to complain about cutting 14 hours from their workweek, especially if it means keeping the same salary?

In regards to staffing, you may need to make a few adjustments to the shifts people work. For instance, with a Straight-6-Schedule, you will work from 7:00 in the morning to 1:00 in the afternoon and then 1:00 to 7:00 on alternate days. Unless of course, you decide to take on an associate or a partner, in which case you'll run all day with two shifts of workers.

By working people hours instead of business hours, you are able to grow your practice even quicker. Now, I know that some of your staff will find it difficult to come in early or work late due to family responsibilities, so you may have to hire fill-ins, but honestly, that isn't usually a major concern. You'll be making so much more revenue on this schedule; it will easily cover any extra overhead personnel costs.

Here's another thing to consider when using Straight-6-Scheduling: your office space. Maybe you are a one-doctor operation and decide to stay that way. That means there will be large chunks of time during the day when your office is closed. Why not consider renting that space to a non-competing type physician or dental specialty like an orthodontist? Of course they would be responsible for bringing in their own staff and supplies (they'd only be using your chairs and most basic equipment) when you are not in the office yourself.

Planning Your Patient's Treatment
While moving toward a Straight-6-Schedule can do wonders for improving your productivity and profits, learning how to plan your patient's treatment better can do the same.

If you want to get things done a little quicker, you may want to consider using fewer appointments. True, this will require looking at dentistry in a whole new way and learning to do things differently, but it certainly can help you get more work done and use up less time slots on your schedule.

Here's a scenario for some fairly time consuming patient needs:
Let's say, for the sake of argument that the patient cannot afford implants and you are going to be doing a partial. Here is the diagnosis: the patient needs to have tooth number 1 extracted, number 2 has a mesial area of decay, number 3 needs a crown, a build up and a root canal. Number 4 needs a crown, number 10 needs a veneer, number 12 needs an MO filling, number 13 needs a filling, number 14 needs an MO, number 16 needs an extraction, number 19 needs a crown, 20 needs an MO and then 21 to 28 bilaterally missing all the teeth from that point distal, 29 needs a filling and then number 30 needs a crown, a build up and root canal. Although the patient can't afford a bridge, he does want his teeth whitened.

Now, how many visits would this take in your office? Most dentists would say five or six (or even more). A good treatment plan can get all of this done in just 3 visits, with a fourth follow-up/delivery appointment.

So, how can you get all of this work done more efficiently? By developing a plan of action that uses your time more efficiently. Here's an example:

During the first appointment you would take impressions for the lower partial and the upper teeth, plus go ahead and make the upper tray for the whitening so you could pre-condition the teeth for the bleaching.

Next, you would prep and fix the teeth with the proper inclines and do the lower impression for the partial and prep number 19 and 30 for crowns. You could also fill number 21 and 29.

Finally, you would do the build up on number 30, do the prep, finish the prep on it and number 19.

During the second appointment, deliver the bleaching tray and get that started. Do the fillings on number 2, 12, 13, and 14 and prep 3 and 4 for crowns and number 10 for the veneer. With the framework back from the partial, you could go ahead and take the bite, so that would be a framework with the wax bite and then at the end of that appointment, remove teeth 1 and 16.

At the third appointment, you would complete the endo on 30 and 3, and deliver all crowns and veneers.

The fourth appointment would be reserved for the partial. Since you will be finishing up the seating on crown number 3, you'll probably have to adjust the partial in that area because the occlusion of 3 is going to be a little bit different from the impressions that you sent.

Finally, during the fourth appointment you could handle any adjustments.

While it may be common to take eight appointments to get this work done, it can – and should – be handled in much less! By combining procedures, you get more accomplished during each visit which is good for both you and the patient.

The key to developing this type of patient plan is looking at the scenario differently, with fewer appointments in mind. Once you begin to see the benefits of doing more with the time you have, it'll get easier and easier to maintain a quick-moving treatment plan for every patient.

By using these simple strategies, you'll soon find that your schedule makes more sense and that your entire office is running more smoothly.

Chapter Eight:

Learning How To Motivate Your Office

What do you think is the number one motivator for your employees? If you answered money, you are not alone in your thinking – but you are off base. Most managers and business owners believe that an employee's top motivation is financial compensation, when in reality most employees would rank being appreciated above money nearly every time. That doesn't mean you can lower all your staff salaries and start giving pats on the back instead of bonuses, but it should focus your thinking a little on what your employees are really looking for and how to motivate them to work to their potential so that your dental practice will realize its potential.

It is the savvy employer who knows how to make the business' success a priority for his or her employers. You may not think of yourself as a business manager. In fact, you may struggle with this part of running your dental practice. After all, you got into dentistry because you loved the clinical side, not so that you would find yourself managing an office full of employees. If you want to grow your practice and be truly successful, you are going to have to wear not just your dentist hat, but the manager's hat as well.

Wouldn't it be great if you had a blueprint for a successful team: a proven method of getting your team from just going through the motions and following directions to being a committed and focused team? Well, we can give you just that!

As we mentioned earlier, most bosses feel that if they are giving their employees fair or even great pay, then their employees will know that they are appreciated. After all, you wouldn't pay them well and give out bonuses if you didn't appreciate them, right? Well, just paying them well isn't really enough.

What will make your employees a dedicated part of your business is making them feel that they are an important part of the practice and that each of them is responsible for the success of the business. It might be your name on the sign, but you can cultivate an atmosphere of dedication amongst your staff that will make it seem like everyone has a stake in the success or failure of your practice.

Let's get down to the nitty gritty of the process, or the 7 steps to a successful team, as Dr. Bill Kimball of the Kimball Consulting company has so aptly named them. His system of staff motivation has proven successful in dental office after dental office all around the country for the last decade!

Step One: Coaching

You are a dentist. You may or may not have learned much about human resources or staff management during your education, and that's okay. Wherever you are starting is just fine and whether you have some expertise in management or not, coaching is vital to your success. When you are running an independent dental practice you are operating in your own little world, and you don't have many resources within your practice for learning about management or how to deal with or motivate your staff.

That is where coaching comes in. Because you are reading this book, you are interested in change and you are open to new ideas and new ways of dealing with your practice. You know that you will only get a new result when you begin to do things in a new way. Being able to seek out some coaching and really take to heart and try to implement the new information is the first step toward changing the tone in your office. If you value your employees, you want them to feel that. You know that they are vital to your success and that they each have an important role to play in the overall working of your office.

Step 2: Building Leadership Skills

You can probably identify the employees in your practice with true leadership ability. It's a quality that can be difficult to quantify, we all know a leader when we see one: their actions speak the most clearly about their abilities. Leaders take charge, they are confident and comfortable making decisions and other people instinctively look to them for guidance. They have an innate integrity and they are self-starters who can see what needs to be done and get about the business of doing it.

Leaders are also not control freaks. A true leader does not have to do it all themselves, and that is as true for your staff as it is for you. Leadership means taking the helm of the ship and guiding it where it needs to go; it does not mean that you are going to do every single task that needs to be done on the ship, even down to the cooking! A leader knows when to let people do the work they are good at and when to step in and provide guidance.

You will want to develop your own leadership abilities as you continue to work on motivating and energizing your staff. Learn to listen to them, really let them know that you understand where they are coming from and what they need and want from you. Be ready to provide support and guidance, but also know when to step back and let your employees do their jobs. No one wants to work with their boss over their shoulder every minute of the day and doing that to your employees will only make them feel that you don't trust them or have faith in their abilities.

Just as you are cultivating your own leadership abilities, you should be evaluating your staff to determine who the leaders are. If you have someone with leadership ability working for you, you can develop a relationship with them that will help him/her lead the office staff. If your front desk manager has leadership qualities, then he/she will also be able to motivate the rest of the staff and you should be recognizing him/her for her talents.

Keep in mind that your employees are looking for WIIFM: *What's In It For Me?* In all situations. They want to feel that they are part of the big picture for the practice, not just that they are there to punch a clock and pick up a paycheck. If you can use your leadership skills to get everyone on board together, you will see great benefits in employee morale and motivation!

A leader keeps learning and growing and isn't afraid to look for outside resources for help. Although you may posses a lot of natural leadership ability, that doesn't make you an expert in all fields. With some coaching, you can harness your inherent leadership skills and put them to work for your dental practice!

Step 3: Communication
Communication is so simple and so essential that it may be the most important part of motivating your staff. If you value your staff, but don't know how to communicate that to them, all your good intentions will get you nowhere. If you are interested in making changes to the way your office functions or are implementing a new bonus system, but don't know how to effectively communicate with your staff, you may breed contempt right in your own office. Knowing what to say, when to say it and most importantly, how to say it, will be the key to successfully motivating your staff and putting you all on the same path to growth and prosperity.

The first thing we think of with communication is the spoken word, but body language and attitude play a huge part in the communication you have with your staff and your patients. Making eye contact, taking the time to stop what you are doing while speaking and even something as simple as sitting down to speak to your staff can all go a long way towards getting your message heard. We could really devote an entire chapter to body language, it's that vital to communication, but suffice it to say that your ability to get your voice heard has as much to do with your demeanor as it does with your words. Whether it's talking to a patient or getting your staff on board with some new ideas, take a moment to check your body language and be sure it's welcoming, open and comfortable.

It's also important to remember that communication is a two way street. Just as you are going to try your best to make your message heard, you will want to keep the lines of communication open for your staff. If everyone on your team feels comfortable coming to you with suggestions, ideas and yes, even problems, you are well on your way to having a highly motivated and very productive team!

DISC: The Types Of Communication
DISC is a Performance System and Survey that will give you detailed information on yourself and your staff. While we can't get into all the specifics here in this chapter, just a little insight into how the system works and what benefits the system would have for motivating your staff will go a long way to helping you understand why communication is a biggie when it comes to dealing with, and more importantly energizing your staff.

The DISC system categorizes people into four main personality types: D-dominant, I-Influencer, S-Steadiness and C-Conscientious. As we are listing these types you are probably already picking out the people in your office and in your life and putting them into the category you think would suit them. Knowing this information helps you connect with each personality type on its own terms. You can use what you know about their traits to help you communicate more effectively with them.

D: the dominant personality: A person with a high "D" score will be very motivated by being challenged and they worry most about losing control. Every business should have at least one type D person and that person will most likely be the natural leader in the group. Too many of these and you will have an explosive situation because they all want to take control!

I: the influencer: This person is very social, has great team spirit and thrives on social recognition; they fear rejection.

If your scheduling person and your front desk staff is rich with type I people, you will have a welcoming office atmosphere but they may not get too much done because they are too social. Your office needs the influencer to keep morale high and be a team builder, but you will also need the next two types to keep this one on track.

S: Steadiness: This personality type is the workhorse. Dr. Kimball finds in his consulting business that about 80% of dental office employees fall into this category. These consistent performers keep things running smoothly, but sometimes they resist change. They need an influencer to make the first move when change is coming and then they can follow along.

C: Conscientious: The bean counter of your office, this detail loving, analytical person is the quintessential CPA and if you have one of this type doing your books, you will be well served. They are organized and love to keep things in order.

The dominant personality and the influencer are what we would refer to as "direct," meaning that you can just simply approach a person of these types and let them know what you need, or what isn't running well. Of course, even these two appreciate some positive reinforcement, so remember to temper any criticism with a healthy dose of praise.

Approach S and C types in a more indirect way; they avoid confrontation whenever possible. They are much more likely to feel under attack when issues are brought up and discussing issues with them may take a little more time and tact.

Whatever your style and your employees' styles of communication, the important thing is to work on it. It will always be worthwhile to put the effort into communicating more effectively and you will see a payoff in morale as soon as you make some improvements!

Step 4: The Mission Statement

You may not think of your dental practice as having a mission statement, but not only should you have one, you should make it as public as possible. It may sound corny, but having a visual reminder of what your business stands for and strives to achieve will keep you and your employees more focused on your goals.

As you are going about your business over the next several days, be sure to look around you at the places you frequent. The local fast food restaurant, a movie theater, a doctor's office or even your child's little league game. You may be surprised how many of these places have some kind of a mission statement posted in a public area. Seeing it in writing is powerful and taking the time to figure out what yours is and writing it down will be empowering.

A mission statement is not a simple declaration of what you do – that would be too simplistic and even boring. None of your patients want to read things like "increase production," or "do more quadrant dentistry" or even "sell the patient on a treatment plan!" Your mission statement is not a list of goals or incentives; it is about the ideas of your practice. Your desire to help people, your goals regarding customer service or putting frightened patients at ease – and making dental care affordable for everyone –
those are the items that should be in your mission statement.

Once you have developed the statement, make it public! Post it where staff and patients can read it; put it on a coffee mug if it helps you focus on what is truly important to your practice. Keeping the reasons why you wanted to be a dentist close at hand will certainly help you get through the rougher days that are inevitable in any business.

Step 5: Integrity

Integrity is a virtue and is defined as: the quality of possessing and steadfastly adhering to high moral principles or professional standards. You are asking your patients to trust their health and appearance with you and you are asking your employees to trust the well being of their families with you. After all, if you are a person of integrity, your staff can count on you to run the practice in an honest way.

There is something to be said for that in today's society where it isn't unheard of that a practitioner would be taking money from his own business and leave his employees and patients high and dry. Living your life and running your practice with integrity will motivate your staff to follow your example. If you have high standards for dealing with vendors and insurance companies, your staff will follow suit. Keep your business above reproach and you will have the admiration of your staff.

Step 6: A Written Office System
We've talked about all the touchy-feely parts of motivating your staff, basically how to treat them and how to listen to them. Now, let's get down to the part of motivation that most successful dentists already understand: bonuses. Whatever the bonus system is in your office, you need to ask yourself a few questions. Is it working? Does it motivate my staff? And, possibly most important, is it a reliable system that everyone understands?

As a manager of an office staff, you obviously want to compensate your employees for their hard work and extra effort, but if your bonus system seems arbitrary and isn't tied into your team goals and your mission statement, or if a lack of communication between you and your staff makes it seem slanted toward hygiene rather than the front office, all your efforts may be wasted. Having a clear and written office system and a concise bonus system will keep everyone on the same page when it comes to production and collections goals and will give your employees some great incentives and a positive attitude about their contribution to the team goals.
So, how do you set up a consistent bonus system? It all starts with the breakeven point. You will need to look at your P&L statements, and maybe consult with your

bookkeeper to determine the monthly amount where you have "broken even." This will take into account all your expenses, including rent or mortgage, salaries, and lab fees. If your breakeven point is $50,000, then let your staff know that they will be paid a bonus once you collect anything above that amount. The staff will split 20% above the breakeven point and a great way to do it is to calculate a bonus per day, if all of your staff is full time.

This way, whether the bonus ends up being $10 a day or $100 a day, then each employee will be paid a bonus depending on how many days they work in a month. If you are handing out $100 a day, your part time assistant who works 2 days a week will get an $800 bonus, while your front desk manager will be receiving $2,000! That will be one happy group and just think about your bonus because you will be getting about 50% of the overage for yourself, after taking out additional expenses!

Once you have set the breakeven amount and presented it to your staff, try to keep it consistent for as long as possible. Changing it every month or raising it as collections increase may be tempting, but messing with the bonus is a sure way to breed contempt and unrest among your staff. If your employees know what the bonus point is and what they can do to help the office reach it, they will be motivated to stay focused on the goal. If they feel that the bonus is a carrot always being moved just out of reach, they won't be very interested in trying to get it at all.

It may be difficult for you to share the financial information of your practice with your staff, but by making them feel included in the workings of the business, you are giving them a stake in its eventual success or failure. They will hold a role similar to stockholders in a company: they will succeed when the business succeeds. Only, in contrast to a shareholder, your employees can have a positive effect on the bottom line and on their own eventual income.

Just as you have posted your mission statement, so should you post your collections goals and your break-even point. It's a good idea to keep the goal in mind while you are working and to give your staff ideas on how to make their goals. If broken appointments have been dragging down your practice, a goal of 100% appointment attendance is something your front office staff can get behind. If they are looking at the goal all month and they know where the practice is in relation to the goal, they will be more likely to see it as an incentive. An arbitrary bonus won't motivate your staff, and may be seen as unfair or slanted. Having a written office and bonus system will make each person on your staff feel valued and motivated!

Step 7: Training

We have already talked about coaching, so why do we also need to discuss training? Well, training is something that can benefit your entire staff and make sure that you are all on the same page as far as treatment, office matters and bonus systems. If you are managing a staff of ten people and each of them is going about their business, doing their jobs well, but not communicating with you or each other, it is amazing what could be going wrong. Taking the time to meet with your staff and provide ongoing training will benefit the entire practice in the long run.

Pick a time in the middle of the week, and set aside an hour for staff training. It may seem counterintuitive to take time away from seeing patients to spend in training, but just that small amount of time will pay big dividends in increased production and better employee morale and motivation. If you select a mid-day hour, when appointments are generally light anyway, and spend some time with case presentation techniques, customer service or dental techniques, your whole staff will benefit.

If you have open communication with your staff, you may be surprised what they want to share with the rest of the staff or what they are interested in learning. You could even rely on different departments to provide the training for a week so that you can really understand what is important to them and what they have to contribute.

Keep the information interesting and the tone upbeat and you will find that your staff may begin to look forward to the training sessions as a welcome break to their normal workweek. You don't want your employees to feel that the training time is a punishment or that you are training them because you don't think they can do their jobs. You want to provide continued learning opportunities for yourself and your entire staff.

Ready, Set, Motivate!

While monetary compensation is important and is the main reason people go to work every day, there is so much more to motivating your staff. Being mindful of the individual and learning how to communicate effectively with different personality types is just the beginning of a new and vibrant office atmosphere. If you can begin to implement the 7 steps to motivating your dental practice, you will see results that may surprise you. Go from an efficient office staff to a motivated, committed team and see where it takes your practice!

Chapter Nine:

Managing For Success

We've talked a bit about motivating your staff, but what about *managing* them: there is a difference. Learning to manage your staff and keep problems at bay can go a long way toward building a happy, satisfying workplace for all.

When you entered the field of dentistry, you were probably enticed by the idea of helping people, and you were hoping to make a great living doing something that really spoke to you. Sound familiar? Were you also looking forward to managing a staff of anywhere from 2-22 people? You, like many dentists, may have been unprepared for the pitfalls and challenges that come along with the business side of the dental world and you may be in need of some help.

If you are just starting out in your career and have only a few employees, now is the time to set some ground rules and get your office culture headed in the right direction. Don't worry, we can direct you and help you build your office and your management style from the ground up. If you are frustrated with either doing everything yourself or with no one doing what you want, we are here to help. It is never too late to turn a problem into a solution and we can show you simple, effective and easy-to-implement ways to get your staff on the same page with you and have you all working as a cohesive team. Once your staff hits its stride, you will be off and running toward a successful, peaceful and productive practice.

As we mentioned, there are generally two types of management styles in place in an office that isn't working up to its potential. The hands-on style that is characterized by micro-managing, and the hands-off style which is very popular because many dentists are far more interested in the clinical side of their practice and haven't taken the necessary time to invest in a managerial style. Managing your staff will only get easier when you are ready to accept some new tools and apply them to your business. Then, you can expect some different results!

When your entire practice is running smoothly, you won't be constantly worrying about staff concerns or have to check up on work that should be done. If you become a good manager and an effective communicator, your staff will feel both responsible for the practice's success and empowered to use their skills to their full potential. The first step in motivating your staff is managing them well. Once your office is running smoothly, you can motivate your employees to take your practice to new heights.

The Micro-Manager vs. The Non-Manager
Management styles vary from person to person, but there seems to be a continuum from the micro-manager who wants to get in the middle of everything and the hands-off manager who feels that his staff is intelligent and skilled and can handle things on their own.

The micro-manager can make life miserable for everyone. You cannot concentrate on the clinical side of your dental practice and still have your hand in every part of your business. You also cannot leave your employees to their own devices and hope that everything will be okay. You are the leader, the director, and the manager of your dental practice. If you can find the happy medium between over and under managing your staff, they will appreciate your guidance, seek your approval and appreciate your honest communication. Under management breeds chaos and micro-management breeds frustration.

If you aren't sure which end of the spectrum you fall on, just consider for a moment how your employees are feeling. When you give direction, do you give not quite enough information, leaving them confused and worried about fulfilling your request? Or, alternately, so you keep such a close eye on them and give more details than they could ever possibly need, leading them to feel like a child with an overbearing parent? It may be difficult to take an honest look at your management style, but if you want to take your practice to the next level of success, the secret lies in your ability to effectively manage your staff.

What about when conflicts arise? What is your protocol for handling the difficulties that will inevitably occur when you have a staff? If you are under-managing, you will dread any type of conflict because you don't have a plan in place for dealing with problems. And, likely the only time you take the time to manage your staff is when there *is* a problem. Your office staff won't be happy to hear that you are calling a staff meeting because they know the axe is about to fall. If you are a micro-manager, your staff is probably on eggshells because you have become overly critical. The other drawback of micro managing is that your staff may become lazy and unwilling to make decisions or give suggestions because they have become accustomed to always doing it your way.

If you haven't already concluded, there is a middle ground. There is a way to guide without bossing, to empower without completely letting go. Once you've learned the 5 principles of staff management, you will be able to manage your staff successfully. The principles are: defining success, delegating, choosing your practice's culture, insisting on accountability, and finally becoming a good coach. Let's begin!

Define Success
Imagine you just got hired for a new job. The interview didn't tell you much except that you would be working in an office and everyone seemed really nice. You show up for your first day and someone shows you to your desk and wishes you good luck. As she walks away, you realize you don't have any idea what you are supposed to do or how you should go about doing it.

Could you be successful? Would you even know what it meant to be successful in such a situation? Sure, you are smart and talented and you are excited to get to work, but you are confused and not sure where to start. Not a great first day.

Okay, so that is an extreme example, but just think about how well your goals and expectations are quantified, updated and tracked for your employees. If you have given them a goal for keeping appointments and avoiding broken appointments, do they have the tools they need to get that job done? Do you share your production goals with your hygiene staff or share the information you've learned at conferences with your clinical staff? You may have all the great ideas in the world, but until you have given your staff clear direction, they won't be able to implement them.

Ginny Hegarty of the Institute for Leadership and Accountability shared the following example with us:

One of my favorite doctors in the world attended an Office Magic seminar... he's very excited to bring (all the wonderful resources) back to the practice. He brought them to his office manager, Karen, and told her all about them. Then, as an afterthought, he went back and said "Karen, by the way, I would also like to eliminate billing." Well that's one of the Office Magic philosophies, providing fabulous service while eliminating billing.

Karen didn't make the connection so when I go in to meet the doctor and Karen and the rest of the staff a month or so later, the doctor said to me, "Ginny, I'm so excited to tell you that we've eliminated billing in the practice!" I said,

"I'm shocked; I thought you were sending over 100 statements a month!"

He said, "we were."

So when I met Karen, I said "Tell me, how did you mange to eliminate billing so quickly and easily?"

She just had this very dumbfounded look on her face and said, "I stopped sending bills."

Karen had eliminated billing right off of her task list, but what she didn't do was properly eliminate it by putting different payment options in place. We all had a good laugh about it and the doctor said, "There's a lesson I'll never forget. I didn't make the connection for her."

That dentist certainly learned his lesson the hard way. Giving clear direction to your staff is not micro managing, it's just plain good management. When everyone knows what is expected of them, they will usually exceed those expectations because they are so clearly spelled out.

Delegate Well

First of all, notice that this step is called delegate *well*. While it can be hard for a successful person to learn to let go of even small tasks, effectively delegating responsibility to others is one of the marks of a true leader. Unlike the under-manager who just lets everything slide, a manager who can delegate well knows what to delegate, when to delegate, and most importantly, to whom they should delegate certain tasks. Delegation is interconnected with defining success because if you are able to give everyone clear direction and goals, you will also succeed at delegation. When everyone understands their part of the big picture, they are able to complete whatever their individual job is and complete it well.

You know that your employees are smart, hard working and enjoy working in your dental practice. (If you don't feel this way, you may have more than just these five principles to evaluate.) Determining which employee can and should handle additional responsibility and when to give them additional duties will be an ongoing process. From your employees' perspective, they will appreciate having your confidence and your guidance.

Delegating differs from micro managing because an effective delegator can recognize abilities in an employee and empower them to use them. When your staff feels valued and trusted, they will rise to the occasion of new responsibility. If you under-manage after delegating, then your employee will feel confused and unsure. Without your confident guidance, he or she may be unable to complete the task they have been given. This will leave them feeling frustrated and you facing problems within your office.

Choosing The Culture In Your Practice

What do we mean when we say that your practice has a culture? Well, the atmosphere that you, as the leader and director of the practice, developed has an almost palpable effect on your staff and your patients. If you create the culture of success, and your staff knows it, you will feel more successful, your staff will strive to be successful and you will all feel empowered by just that environment.

We have all heard about the power of positive thinking and you may think that it's just a bunch of new age junk. What is real, however, is that you will reap what you sow when it comes to the atmosphere in your office. Positive thinking will not work if it is not followed up by positive action, but when the two come together, real results follow.

If you recognize and reward your employees for their achievements and they know that these accolades can be consistently expected, they will work harder to attain them. If you are haphazard about bestowing praise, then your employees will either stop trying to earn it, or they will feel that you are playing favorites. Imagine if everyone could be your "favorite"! Your current favorite would be whoever is doing their job well! Each employee has the same potential for success and when that success becomes the standing atmosphere in your business, get ready for a positive, energized office.

Monetary rewards are like the icing on the cake of a positive work atmosphere. Your employees will work hard if they know that everyone is working hard. They will give great customer service if they understand that nothing less will be acceptable in your office.

In business and in life, you get what you will accept. If you set high standards for yourself and follow through with them, you will be setting an example for your staff and setting the tone of your office. Don't fall into the trap of treating all your employees the same. Just as you wouldn't give all your children the same incentive or punishment, your staff all have different personalities and temperaments. Dr. Pat Wahl shares this example:

The term playing favorites is not even accurate. It's not about friendship, it's not about who you like, it's about performance: it's that simple. If someone says Mary got this special favor, if they think that's because she's my favorite, I would say, "How would you like to be my favorite tomorrow? Great, here is what you'll need to do." It's all about performance.

Insist On Accountability

You are headed in the right direction once you start to implement these principles, but you can't just give some praise, define the parameters of success and hope for the best. You are doing all this work so that you can walk that middle ground between being hands off and being a micro-manager. In between those two extremes lies the secret to a smooth running office, but accountability needs to be a part of the process.

Once your employees know what's expected of them, it is vital to hold them accountable for their performance. Bonuses, team activities and shared goals should all be tied to the performance goals you have established. Accountability is often considered to be a negative, but with planning and regular meetings to create goals, it will be a journey that you take along with your staff all the way to success!

Coaching

Just as the football coach doesn't just show up on game day and tell the players what to do, you will need to be an everyday coach for your staff. Using regular circumstances to coach your team and show your support and recognize their good work will lead perfectly into your staff meetings when you can look at the big picture of what is working in your office and what needs a little tweaking.

If you are involved on a day-to-day basis in talking to your staff and catching them doing a good job, you will be better equipped to take on the challenges that are bound to happen when you are dealing with staff. You don't want to be the "bad news" boss that only has something to say when things go wrong; you want to be involved, interested and committed to the success of your entire practice. Letting your employees know they are part of that success is your most important job.

Some Management Tips And The 3 Magic Words

Everything we have discussed about managing your staff has been pro-active. If you implement these ideas into your dental practice, you will see the results over time and you will be able to cultivate the kind of caring, dynamic and successful environment for your staff and yourself that you always hoped was possible.

When a problem arises, and it will, there are several ways to handle it. The micro-manager would get right into the middle of two co-workers who are having a disagreement or try to get to the bottom of every minor problem. The under-manager would just throw up his hands and hope for the best, unwilling or incapable of finding a way to handle disputes and conflict. You cannot afford to go to either of these extremes when it comes to handling conflict in your office. If you allow yourself to get dragged into every dispute, you are doing no one a favor. If you stay out of everything, you will be reinforcing the idea that everyone already has: you aren't invested in what happens right under your nose.

When something does go wrong, take a minute to evaluate the situation and see if you have any responsibility. Were your expectations for your employees clear, or like the doctor from our earlier example, did you give an order without taking the time to connect with your staff? Similarly, if you are dealing with difficult personalities with your staff, are you cultivating a culture of mutual respect in your office? Do you talk to some of your staff about other staff members? That kind of behavior will encourage your employees to talk negatively about one another and, not surprising, of you. If you have developed a culture of respect, that type of gossiping won't be part of your office culture.

Similarly, you can develop a supportive environment where employees feel comfortable addressing problems with each other. When everyone is focused on the work at hand and at providing superior service to patients every day, there will be less worry about interpersonal problems. That is not to say that your practice will be without any problems that would be impossible. What will happen, though, is that you will be creating an atmosphere where grievances can be aired and solutions found together.

Chapter Ten:

Getting The Most From Your Hygiene Department

If your practice isn't expanding like it should, you may want to take a closer look at your hygiene department. It is estimated that a hygienist who is fulfilling her role correctly will bring in between $30,000 and $50,000 in additional revenue per month in re-care cases. If you are shocked to hear those estimates, then your hygiene department is likely not doing its job!

So, how can a good hygiene department bring so much business into your practice? By allowing her to do what she does best:

Educate Patients

All too often, hygienists (and the doctors they work for) believe that their #1 job is to clean a patient's teeth and hand them off to the dentist for case presentation. This is simply not true. Not only is this a waste of the doctor's time, but it would be counter-productive with many patients.

The hygienist's first priority should always be to educate the patient about their oral health and care. Why should this important aspect of the patient's care fall on the hygienist's shoulders? One of the main reasons is this: they have the time to spend with patients to explain what is going on in their mouths and what the repercussions of non-treatment will likely be. One important note here: hygienists should never diagnosis a patient's problems (it's not only unethical; in many states it's illegal!) but rather, discuss with them what they have discovered and what treatment options the dentist may suggest once they enter the room. This helps to accomplish several things:
  a. The hygienist is doing the job she was trained to do, which makes her feel more valuable and more apt to

work harder to help patients accept the treatments offered.

b. It allows the patient to hear about concerns in a more relaxed setting. Some people can be very intimidated by a dentist waltzing into the room and saying this, this and this needs attention and here is what we're going to do about it.

c. It gives the patient time to think about their options. When your hygienist points out problems as she discovers them throughout her exam, it gives the patient time to digest the information and think about what they would like to do about it.

d. It also reinforces everything the doctor has to say (after all, if 2 people are now seeing the same problem and offering the same treatment plan, the odds are more likely the patient will accept whatever treatment options you offer).

Preparing Patients For The Doctor's Recommendations

One of the main benefits of using your hygienist to prepare your patient for what the doctor will likely recommend is this: most patients don't feel as if a hygienist has anything to gain by presenting or showing them what's going on in their mouth. If the hygienist says the doctor will likely recommend a root canal to save the tooth, they are more apt to accept the hygienist's suggestion than the dentist's.

Plus, having your hygiene department properly prepare patients can be a real time saver for the dentist. After all, if it takes him/her half an hour to present a case, that's a half hour they aren't doing real dental work. You need to be able to help the patient want what they need, and the best way to do that is to have your hygienist point out problems as they go along, and explain what other issues those problems can cause in the future and how the dentist will likely want to treat them.

Helping To Convince Patients About Procedures In A More Easy-Going And Non-Threatening Manner Than They May Feel With A Dentist

Patients aren't the least bit threatened by a hygienist. They understand that it's their job to point out concerns and usually don't feel as if the hygienist is trying to sell them something they don't need – a feeling many people get from a dentist. Of course, hygienists don't want to be salespeople either, which makes their presentations appear more friendly and helpful to the patient than one coming from the doctor, who will directly benefit from a procedure.

Increasing Profits By Increasing The Amount Of Work Coming Out Of The Department

Most experts agree that less than 20% of new patients actually accept treatment plans offered by dentists, yet when hygienists are the ones to offer the patient treatment options, nearly 80% accept the doctor's treatment options! Amazing! This is just one way that a good hygienist can increase your bottom line.

The second, of course, is the fact that a hygienist is in a good position to educate patients about preventative and cosmetic treatment options that your office may offer. Re-care is a vital component to building your practice, so make sure that your hygiene department is always looking for ways to educate your patients on the many re-care options you offer.

SIDEBAR: *How Perio-Care Can Increase Business*
One of the fastest and easiest ways to get patients back in your door is to begin beefing up your periodontal care system. The fact is, the vast majority of your patients have bleeding and need some sort of perio-after care. Begin stressing the health benefits of good perio-care with both your hygienists (who in turn will present it to your patients), and see how quickly your practice begins to grow. Many doctors are now offering C-reactive blood tests in their offices to show patients their levels of this

dangerous protein in their mouths, which has been linked to serious heart disease and other ailments. Few people will disregard such a warning when faced with the serious health problems poor oral care can cause and will gladly sign up for a good perio-program in order to prevent future illnesses. Plus, your hygienists love offering practical health solutions that benefit their patients and are more likely to try and "sell" these helpful services than high-cost cosmetic procedures that even they may deem unnecessary.

Why It's Important For Your Hygiene Department To Do The Selling

Basically, your patients end up in your office one of two ways: either to have their teeth cleaned by your hygiene department or because of an emergency. That gives your hygiene department a lot of responsibility to ensure that your business continues to grow and expand. This is done primarily by teaching your hygiene department how to educate your patients about their oral health in order to sell your services.

Most dentists find convincing patients to accept a procedure to be too difficult, often leaving thousands of dollars worth of care sitting idle in your files. The problem with this tactic is the fact that the vast majority of these patients will get that root canal, crown or other procedure you've recommended – the question is, will you be doing it, or will someone else?

One of the reasons you may be finding it difficult to close procedures with patients may be your hygiene department's lack of responsibility in preparing your patients for the outcome you are trying to sell.

One of the biggest mistakes many doctors make is not letting their hygienists do their job properly. Many actually undercut their own hygiene department by telling a patient "we'll just watch that" after the hygienist has prepared the patient for a certain procedure. Check your notes carefully to see what your hygienist has already discussed with your patient, and always confirm their findings. Saying something as simple as, "Yes, I see what Melissa is talking about and here are a few options she may or may not have discussed with you." Your job is not to double-check the work your hygienist has already done, but to confirm their findings with the patient.

Convincing Your Hygiene Department To Sell Your Services

Hygienists are not sales people – and they don't want to be. They want to be oral care providers and educators, so most will balk at the idea of "selling" anything – even necessary procedures. The key to convincing your hygiene department of the necessity of chair sales (and its importance) is to explain how important oral health education is to you – and your patients. Teach them how to properly educate their patients on pre-care and re-care in order to help them better present cases to patients, which in turn, turns into a sale.

No one is suggesting that your hygiene department becomes a high-pressure sales team. What we are suggesting is that you use their expertise to help patients better understand their role in maintaining good oral health – and what to do about it!

If your hygienists understand the importance of preventative perio-care and re-care for problem areas, they'll be in a better position to explain it to your patients.

Turning your hygiene department into a power sales force doesn't mean teaching them how to sell unnecessary procedures; it requires teaching them how to educate your patients on the procedures that will benefit their overall health and well being the most!

Some simple tips your hygiene department can use to accomplish these goals include:
- Disclosing problems to patients right away – never assume that a patient cannot afford treatment. Be sure to always offer to disclose problems, let the doctor offer several treatment options, and even

explain that financing options are available when needed.

- Explaining what other problems an uncared for issue can create. Patients rarely know (or understand) the serious complications an untreated problem can cause. Be sure to be clear and concise about future issues that can be avoided if treatment is accepted.

- Helping the patient own their problem. Be sure to have your hygiene department explain to the patient how any discovered problems could have been avoided and what to do to ensure they don't find themselves with a repeat of the same issue in the future. Once a patient begins to take responsibility for their care, they are more apt to follow through with treatment.

- Outlining several options the dentist may suggest (do nothing and this may happen, do this or do this).

There's no need to be overly assertive and pushy here. The important thing is to give the patient the information they need to make a balanced, educated decision and watch how many say yes to treatment!

Some Of The Services Your Hygiene Department Should Be Urging Patients To Consider

It's obvious for your hygiene department to try and "sell" a filling, root canal or even a crown, but are they also offering patients preventative care services like periodontal scaling, cosmetic procedures like teeth whitening and Invisalign straighteners, or even more comprehensive treatment like bridges, crowns and implants? If not, they are leaving a lot of money on the table while failing to give your patients the most comprehensive care they can. Be sure to urge your hygienists to cover "all of the bases" with each and every patient to ensure proper care as well more re-care sales.

As you can see, a well run hygiene department is essential to maintaining the kind of re-care you'll need to keep your practice growing. Be sure that your hygienists know the important role they play in your practice – and your bottom line.

Chapter Eleven:

Incorporating New Technologies Into Your Practice

Money is tight these days, and as more and more employers cut back on insurance premiums (including dental insurance), many doctors are feeling a squeeze to their bottom line. So, how can you not only survive this (or any) economic downturn, but manage to thrive in it? One way may be to add a few new technologies to your practice.

Now, before you worry that adding services will only increase your overall costs, consider these startling statistics:
- 30% of Americans ages 55 and over have no teeth (that's over 26 million people!).
- Less than 1% of people with dentures have received implant therapy
- Most patients over the age of 55 pay using cash
- This denture crowd really appreciates what you do for them and are twice as likely to refer their acquaintances to your practice as any other patient group.

As the population ages, the demand for denture and implant services will only increase, so why not be at the forefront of these new technologies? The doctors who begin now to add denture and implant services to their offerings will be that much further ahead, having the time to build their reputation and experience as others lag behind this growing service curve.

For some smaller office dentists, the cost of equipment and training to add traditional implants to their service offerings is prohibitive, but that doesn't mean that you can not reap the benefits of less invasive procedures like mini-implants and dentures.

There are a lot of benefits to catering to this "denture crowd." First and foremost, there are a lot of them. With numbers in the millions nationwide, this is a patient category that you simply cannot afford to overlook. Besides, senior citizens are wonderful patients to work with. In most cases they are very patient and reliable, pay on time, and truly appreciate good work. Plus, they are wonderful avenues for referrals – the basis of any good practice.

According to statistics, the more mature patient is more likely to show off (and talk up) your work than any other demographic group. That includes their friends who need similar work done, their children and grandchildren who may be interested in popular veneers and teeth whitening services, and others who are in need of basic dental care.

Now, dentures don't seem to be a favorite among many dentists, but there is a new procedure that can both make treating denture patients easier, but also increase your bottom line tremendously: mini-implants. A great option for those who have grown tired of having their dentures relined regularly, but who are not good candidates for traditional full implants (or simply can not afford their hefty price tag), mini-implants are easier to put in, less stressful for the patient, demand less ridging, are less expensive, and require regular maintenance – just like natural teeth and regular implants.

Not well known thus far, mini-implants are growing in popularity, both with patients and with doctors. At more than half the price of traditional implants, they offer the patient the opportunity to have a few small (less invasive) implants put in to better hold their dentures in place. With mini-implants, most patients report a major decrease in slippage, soreness and realignment problems than they previously experienced with their current dentures, giving them a more natural feel.

To determine if a patient is a good candidate for mini-implants, ask these simple questions:
- Are your dentures loose?
- Are you embarrassed by your dentures?
- Do you need to use sticky or messy adhesive?
- Do you have trouble eating?
- Do you experience sore spots often?

Mini-implants benefit a lot of patients who wouldn't otherwise qualify for standard implants including the medically compromised and those who simply cannot handle a more invasive procedure. They are also relatively quick and can be immediately loaded (unlike traditional implants which take months of healing and site preparation), plus they are very cost efficient. The cost to the average dentist nationwide is about $60 for each implant and an additional $60 for the housing, yet most charge about $775 for each implant and $185 for the housing. A much cheaper option for the patient, yet much more profitable for the dentist than simple dentures!

Marketing Mini-Implants To Your Patients

Marketing this lesser known dental option isn't difficult, although it must target a specific group: preferably, older denture wearers. There are three marketing ploys that seem to work well with this demographic:
- The Buy 3, Get 1 Free Option -- For some reason older patients love this deal and are quick to pick a dentist who offers this option, although it usually costs the same as buying the mini-implants separately. Basically it works like this: you figure out how much you must get for a full set of four mini-implants (since most people need four to keep their dentures in place), and divide that number by three instead of four; advertising a Buy 3, Get 1 Free Special. Of course, those who need less than four will be paying a higher rate for individual implants, but you can always offer a different type of discount for them if you'd like.
- A 10% discount. Seniors love a discount, so many dentists have begun offering a 10% discount (which

they have factored into the price already), in order to pull in those bargain hunters.
- The Free Consultation – honestly, a mini-implant consultation doesn't take much time (less than 20 minutes), and usually results in at least a $100 Panorex fee for those who are good candidates. Many dentists are now offering this free option as a way to get more people in to see what the mini-implants are all about.

Another great way to tell people about this new service is to offer to give a short half hour presentation at a local independent living facility or senior center. For the cost of some doughnuts, coffee and your time you may be able to meet with dozens of prospective patients. If just one signs on for the mini-implants, you've made more than $3,000 in profits! That's not a bad return on this marketing investment.

Why are mini-implants so popular among the older, more mature crowd? For one thing, they require a much less invasive procedure, which of course means less time in the dental chair as well as recuperation/healing. Plus, they seem to match the $10,000 price point most seniors feel comfortable paying. Research has shown that people over 60 are most comfortable paying less than $10,000 for any type of non-essential procedure. Go above that number and they often argue that they "won't live long enough to get their money back." That may be why so many older folk dismiss the idea of traditional implants.

Another benefit that the dentist sees from mini-implant patients is the continual revenue they produce. Once you change a denture patient into an implant patient, you have created an ongoing source of income. Implant patients come in for regular checks and maintenance (such as an evaluation of the implant and an o-ring change or housing change of the denture), just like patients who need care done on their natural teeth. With a charge of $75 for this basic 10-15 minute appointment every six months, having dozens of these types of patients being treated every month can be a real financial boost for a struggling practice.

As you can see, there are several ways to increase profitability, while still managing to offer services that people want – and need. The key is to look at your local community demographics and see what type of people live in your community and what types of services they will likely need in the future.

Chapter Twelve:

Getting Control Of Your Office Finances

From collecting past due accounts; developing effective billing procedures to offering patient financing and finding creative ways to get the cash flowing in your office, this chapter is designed to answer all of your office finance questions.

But, first, let's talk a bit about creating a cash surge in your office – after all, who couldn't use a bit of extra cash?

Quick Ways To Generate Cash
Did you know that there are five things that you can do right now to create an instant cash surge in your practice? Well, there are!

Establish An Accounts Receivable Reduction Plan -- Most dentists have long lists of patients who have owed them money for weeks, months, and sometimes even years. Isn't it time that you got serious about collecting that money! Look at it this way: if you file even $300 worth of unpaid bills every month, which could mean $3,600 in a single year of uncollected revenue – and let's face it, most of you reading this book have stacks of unpaid bills worth much more than that!

The first step to collecting these unpaid bills is to assign a point person to sit down and make some phone calls. Now, this can be one of your receptionists or even your office manager, just be sure that when the point person is handling collection calls, they aren't responsible for anything else – answering phone, making appointments, sending out bills, etc. Hide them away in a small private office that is quiet and make sure that everyone in the office understands that they cannot be disturbed – no matter what.

Next, you'll want to sit down with your collections caller and sift through those unpaid bills, dividing them into two stacks: one with people you know are going to pay you, but are just awaiting insurance claims, etc. Good patients who've simply put off making that payment will often respond immediately once you pick up the phone to gently remind them of their bill. As a matter of fact, nearly 75% of these patients will either give you a credit card number immediately, or agree to settle their bill within a few days. That's why you begin with these patients – they offer instant success!

The second stack will consist of people that you have doubts about. You aren't exactly sure why they haven't paid, so they may need a bit more prompting. This may entail a friendly reminder call from your point person to find out if there is a reason why they haven't paid their bill (and to help them figure out an acceptable alternative), followed by a letter outlining what they owe and any agreement which was reached over the telephone.

The best tactic to use with these patients is to offer one of these financing options:
- Immediate payment, at which time they'll receive a 5% courtesy discount
- Help obtaining third-party patient financing… email Woody at woody82647@aol.com for a complete list of outside financing companies
- Setting up an in-house payment plan that features a date in which their bill will be paid in full

If you are like most dentists, you may worry that pushing non-payers to indeed pay their bills may cause them to leave the practice, but look at it this way: right now you are offering interest-free loans to these patients, and if they have no intention of paying you for your services anyway, are they really the type of patient you want – and need – for your practice?

Start Charging Properly For Lab Bills. This is an area where most dentists lose money – lots and lots of money. It's important to establish a good lab ratio (about 5 to 7 times the amount of your lab bill) in order to make the kind of profits that you need to sustain and grow your practice. That means that if the lab charges you $100 for a crown, you must charge your patient between $500 and $700 for that crown.

Start Offering Adult Fluoride. By simply adding adult fluoride to your treatment plan can generate $18,000 to $40,000 in additional revenues for the average one-doctor practice – with virtually no overhead costs! Look at it like this, if only four patients a day agree to accepting adult fluoride treatments at $23 each, your practice will rake in more than $18,000 in extra revenue every year – and the odds are your hygiene department is treating more than 4 patients a day!

But is adult fluoride necessary? Absolutely! As patients get older, their teeth become more prone to decay, especially at the edges of fillings and crowns and at the gum line. Be sure that your hygienist explains this. Although insurance usually does not cover the cost of adult fluoride, most patients eagerly agree to the service when they consider the alternative – possibly paying for an expensive filling later on.

The important thing to remember when offering patients this important service is to:

- Address the insurance up front (letting them know it is not covered)
- Explaining the benefits adult fluoride can offer (extra protection in compromised area)
- Making an assumptive close (asking, "so what flavor would you like?")

You will be amazed at how well this sell works and how much money it can produce for the practice.

Offering Adult Sealants. Like fluoride, many adult patients never consider having sealants put on their teeth for added protection. The fact is, every tooth that does not have a restoration should be sealed, to prevent further decay or damage. At a cost of $9 to $41 per tooth, sealants are much less expensive than fillings or crowns.

Begin the sealant sell by hanging a sign in your hygiene operatories that says, "A tooth without a sealant is like a car without a seatbelt." This usually peaks the patient's curiosity enough to ask about the importance of sealants, which gives you the opportunity to offer its benefits without appearing to be trying to sell them something.

Now, when it comes to profits, sealing just eight teeth per day for 200 days will produce $65,000 in extra production for the office in just one work year. If you place 16 sealants a day, you'll make another $130,000 every year without any extra work or expense. Plus, you'll be offering your patients a much-needed service.

Save Money By Eliminating Credit Card Fees. Research estimates that nearly 40% of outstanding dental bills are now paid using a credit card. What many dentists don't realize is that there are several ways to cut down (or even eliminate) those high credit card transaction fees, and save their office thousands of dollars every year!

According to Leo Townsend of International Payment Solutions, many credit card companies are bilking doctors for thousands in excess transaction fees by making their systems so complicated. While a doctor may think he's paying a 1% processing fee, he's really paying 3 or 5%! That's a big chunk of change.

"Most dentists can expect to receive at least a 20% reduction in rate fees when using our service," explains Townsend, "but even those who decide to go it alone can reduce their costs simply by educating themselves about their carriers and how they work."

The first thing a dentist must do is take a good look at their monthly statement (or have a company like International Payment Solutions evaluate it for you 888-458-1959). That's the only way to determine what they are paying for each type of card accepted in their office.

The first thing you want to avoid is paying a flat fee instead of a transaction fee. Why? Simple. While you may balk at paying a $1.00 processing fee for every credit card accepted in your office, consider the alternative, paying a percentage (even a small one) on the total amount of the bill. Considering the fact that the average dental bill runs between $200 and $300, paying a minimal 2% flat fee would cost you $2.00 - $3.00 for each transaction (with higher bills costing you much more). Plus, if you don't key in a card number correctly (and how many times a day does that happen?), you could get stuck paying another 2% fee. At least with a flat transaction fee like 75 cents or $1, you will only be billed another 75 cents or $1 to run the number a second time.

Now, let's talk about debit cards. Many of these can be used as credit or debit. Well, if you have a pin pad in your office, you can save that transaction fee by asking the patient to punch in their security code vs. using it as a credit card. That's a few more dollars in your pocket.

The other nice benefit about debit cards is that they take the money from the patient's account immediately, giving you no reason to worry about bounced checks.

Getting Paid, Right Away
Now that you've learned a few ways to increase your cash flow immediately, let's look at the most important aspect of your office finances: ***getting paid*** – *right away.*

As we've already discussed, most dentists have a pile of unpaid bills littering their files. True, assigning someone to handle collections can indeed reap the rewards of sudden cash, wouldn't it be much better to get paid right away and never have to worry about patient collections? Of course it is, but how do you go about ensuring that every patient pays as they go? There are some solid strategies that can be used to help eliminate having too many (if any) unpaid patient bills at the end of the month.

Keep A Credit Card File On Every Patient
More often than not, an unpaid bill is due to an insurance issue, leaving the patient owing a balance they may not have even been aware of. This can also cause ill will with patients, since many have already paid a certain amount and feel as if they are being double billed.

One way to avoid this confusion is to require that they keep a valid credit card number on file. The best way to present this to patients is to start by saying something like, "May we keep a credit card number on file for you in the event your insurance overpays so we may credit your account?" It's always nicer to begin the request by saying something about crediting their account instead of charging to it. Then you can finish with the, line, "Or to charge your account if we receive less than we originally thought." That way they know you will charge them for any difference between what the insurance pays and what is owed, but it doesn't seem as if your only intent in holding their credit card information is to charge their account.

Once a patient agrees to keep their credit card information on file, you no longer have to worry about sending out bills or handling collections. Their bills are paid promptly because you are the one handling payments, not them.

Offer Payment Plans. Instead of keeping a running tally of bills owed, another good way to ensure prompt (and regular) payment is to come up with a payment plan that requires patients to make a certain payment amount on a specific day each month. This can be done by applying the monthly charge to their credit card; automatically withdrawing it from their checking account (or debit card) or even cashing pre-dated checks, which they leave with you at the time of service. This way, the patient doesn't have to "remember" to write a check or drop off their payment, and you don't have the hassle of sending bills and making collection calls.

One side benefit that the payment plan offers is the ability to sell your services on a smaller more manageable basis. For instance, it is a lot easier to convince a patient to agree to a procedure at a cost of $300 a month for four months, than to agree to a $1,200.00 procedure. For some patients, that $1,200 price tag is too much to overcome, but they can see the benefit of spending $300 for a few months.

Avoid Insurance Confusion
Insurance can be very confusing. Every carrier offers different benefits, and sometimes what we think is covered may or may not be what we anticipated. This can leave a patient feeling very overwhelmed, and sometimes a bit too skittish to even agree to a procedure. That's why it is important to find a way to explain how insurance works in an easy and manageable way. Many dentists have found using preprinted explanation benefits helpful. Designed to offer simple answers to a patient's most complex insurance questions, the pamphlet can be used as a way to educate the patient about their insurance coverage and their financial responsibilities. It can also be used very efficiently to diffuse a crisis. Let's say a patient thinks you said one thing about their insurance coverage, you can simply refer them back to the pamphlet, where everything is written clearly.

Offer Pay As You Go Services
Another way to help patients better handle the cost of larger procedures is to avoid giving computer estimates for the entire procedure, instead telling the patient from appointment to appointment what is owed. This can be beneficial in several ways:
- The patient doesn't get overwhelmed by a big price tag
- They can better handle smaller payments
- You aren't stuck with unpaid balances on your books

It's always much easier to tell the patient. "This is what you'll need to pay for the next visit," period. Nothing about the procedure cost or what the insurance will pay. Basically they don't care anyway, they just need to know what they'll be responsible for the next time they walk through the door.

Offer Financing Cards
Outside financing cards are another great tool to use to ensure that your patients can get the service they need and you get paid. Of course, there are dozens of different types of cards you can offer your patients. Some are very good and some are not. Some dentists look for the lowest discount rate they can find, only to discover that most of their patients don't qualify for the card. That doesn't help your patients, but you may be balking at the idea of paying 15, 18 or 20% discount on the cards most patients qualify for.

Here is where you get around those high fees: you get the patient to pay more upfront by saying something like, "Congratulations Mrs. Jones, you've been approved for financing as long as you put down $500 you've been approved for the other $500 by the health card and you can go forward with treatment."

Now, what did you accomplish with that statement? You changed the amount that the patient is actually putting on the card from $1,000 to $500. You helped the patient and now they only have to come up with half of your fee upfront, and you're only paying service fees on $500 instead of $1,000. Of course, if the patient can't come up with half the money due, you can scale it back to 30% or 20% or whatever meets their needs. The point is, anything you can get the patient to pay for upfront is less that you'll be charged in finance fees from the health card company.

Now, one important note here: never give a patient an annual percentage rate on these health cards. Always present as either a monthly percentage rate or a monthly service fee. Why? Because saying they'll be charged an

18% annual percentage rate sounds much higher than a 1.5% monthly percentage rate or an $8.00 monthly service fee. It's all in the way the patient perceives the fee. While they may decline an 18% rate, most will gladly agree to pay $8 a month on a $1,000 balance.

As you can see, there's plenty of ways to make sure that you get paid for your services that really aren't difficult to implement at all. In most cases it's just a matter of making it easier for the patient, eliminating their need to think about paying their bill by taking care of it yourself.

Chapter Thirteen:

Exit Strategies: How To Plan For Your Retirement

If you are new to the practice of dentistry, you probably haven't given much thought to when or even how you will retire. You are busy building your business, finding new patients, hiring staff and trying to maximize productivity. You are likely putting any profit your practice is making back into the business with the goal of making it a strong, vibrant and enduring practice. You got into dentistry because you wanted to help people, but if you don't also help yourself, you may find that you have very little, if anything, saved for retirement.

If you are at the mid-point or later in your career, you may be like most dentists who have not been able to save toward retirement. You are in good company as most dentists are in the same boat. The average dentist is 52-years-old, with only about $250,000 in net assets; does that sound familiar?

You have been working hard, growing your practice and trying to contain costs, but what has happened? Maybe your lifestyle has gotten ahead of your income or you have allowed the needs and wants of today to get in the way of planning for the future. Whatever the reason, there is still time to prepare for retirement and it may take less time than you could imagine.

Most dentists are able to afford a comfortable living while they are in practice, but unlike in other jobs where the company provides a pension or a retirement plan, you will have to fund these things yourself. If you want to keep living like you are making $100,000-$150,000 a year, you will have to save about three to four million dollars while you are working. That sounds unlikely, doesn't it? You want to be able to reap the benefits of your hard work now, while you are in practice, not save every spare penny so that you can retire someday. Well, as you will soon learn, banking all of your income is not only impractical, it's also unnecessary. When the time comes to retire, you will have a plan to do it the right way, thanks to our proven strategy.

With the right information and motivation, you may even find yourself able to retire early from the clinical practice of dentistry and have an income generating business operating right alongside your current business.

Money Trap #1– The Luxury Car

Our culture is definitely consumer driven, and we all worry about "keeping up with the Joneses." You may have fallen into this common trap yourself, wanting and purchasing one or two luxury cars for the status of owning the best and newest of almost everything. After all, you are a dentist; you can't be seen driving a ten-year-old Toyota Camry, right? You work hard and your profession does allow you some luxuries and you make a good income, but you need to look at the true bottom line of your business. Be sure to treat your dental practice as the business it is and take a hard look at each expenditure. Do you have your goals in mind when you are making a purchase, or are you simply buying what you think you need or what you want in the moment?

Well, you can still have the appearance of affluence without paying the price by purchasing a used car. We all know that new cars lose their value the moment we drive them off the lot, so why purchase an expensive brand new car when you can enjoy the same luxury vehicle, just a bit of an older model? The short answer is status. It feels good to buy a brand new car and you may want to cave to the pressure of having a new car every few years, but once you put your retirement on the front burner, the money you will save through buying used can be put towards your goals rather than your immediate gratification.

A New Way To Retire, With A Profit!

Because the majority of dentists are independent, and running their own practices, there seems to be a myriad of different ways to end a business and retire, but few, if any, dentists, actually make a profit when they do so. Imagine that: building up your practice for literally decades and then leaving with very little to show for all that work.

Commonly, dentists will use a practice broker to sell their business, but the return on this type of sale is minimal and doesn't accurately reflect the worth of the business at all.

Your facility, your equipment and most importantly, your patient base is very valuable and should be considered when you are ready to retire and sell your practice. Just as a "turn-key" operation is worth more than the real estate it occupies, so is your practice worth much more than the brick and mortar location and the cost of equipment. You can, with a new plan and a different mindset, sell your practice over time while you are still working and make more profit than you probably had imagined. The key to this whole concept is planning. You will be working your business as you are retiring and you will be reaping the financial rewards of both your retirement and your work at the same time.

If you have previously hired an associate or two, you know both the benefits and pitfalls to this situation. The associate may be working in your office a few days a week and that arrangement may have worked out great for both of you, providing you with more income for your practice and giving him or her practical experience. Of course, most dentists have had that experience with an associate who just didn't "fit" their practice or who did not uphold the standards of their business.

If you have never added an associate to your practice, be sure to read carefully the information contained in chapter 7 of this book regarding lowering overhead and increasing profit in your practice. The addition of a part-time associate can generate income for your practice, without requiring you to work additional hours, or can allow you to cut back your hours without reducing income. Many dentists who are interested in being part time associates are recent graduates of dental school and want to learn the business end of dentistry or to apprentice with a more experienced person. Also, being a part time associate is a great position for a dentist with small children or one who is retired from their own practice but still wants to see patients. The associate can be a great benefit to your practice. Frequently, you can still increase income even with cutting back your hours!

For the purpose of retirement, however, we will not be seeking associates. Rather, you will want to look for a partner, and eventually several partners. This may seem strange to you, especially because you have spent years building up your practice on your own, not dependent on someone else for your income. Independence may be what you treasure most in your dental practice so you may initially feel reluctant to consider giving that up. Once you understand the process of dividing up your business as a means to retirement, however, you will realize that it is because of your hard work and dedication to your practice that you will be able to achieve financial success by parceling out and selling your business.

Let's get down to the plan for retirement. Rather than take on a part time associate, this plan requires you to find a *partner*, who will have a monetary stake in your practice. We recommend bringing on the first partner at a cost of one half the income of the practice for one year. So, if your practice takes in $600,000 a year, your first partner, we'll call him Dr. Joe for this example, will pay you $300,000 to be a partner in your practice. You will split your hours with him equally and also split the profits. Our detailed plan will give you more specifics on exactly how to value your practice but for the sake of this example, we will base all the amounts on the yearly income figure.

Now, you and Dr. Joe are partners. You can work out of your same facility, providing that you have enough operatories to work together, probably four would work for this scenario. Over the course of several years, you and Dr. Joe will build up an even more lucrative practice-to the tune of $750,000. At that point, you may be prepared to take on a third partner. You will sell one third of the business to Dr. Sue for $250,000 and take her on in the same way you included Dr. Joe. You and Dr. Joe will sell her the third share. At this point, you can cut your own working hours back even further. You are still earning your own income and thanks to your successful partnerships with Dr. Joe and Dr. Sue, you are working fewer hours, while still bringing in a good income. Plus, you have money in the bank thanks to the sales of the partnership stakes in your practice.

If you have followed this far, let's take it a step further. You are now 5 years into your retirement process, you have two partners and your practice is producing around one million dollars a year. It's time to bring in another partner at a price of, you guessed it, $250,000, one third of which is yours to keep! At this point, you are the senior partner in the practice you built from the ground up. Your partners have reaped the benefits of your years of experience and the time, effort and concern your entire staff has spent building up a patient base. When Dr. Kim joins your thriving practice, you are able to be simply working part time in your own business yet still making nearly as much, if not more than you did when you worked full time hours, thanks to the partnership structure you have created.

You are retiring on your own terms and with a nice profit –just as you should be after spending your career developing a successful practice and creating important connections with patients and businesses along the way. If you begin the process late in your career, you can speed up the timetable to suit your needs and your desire to retire. If you have learned this system early in your career, you will have the tools necessary to plan for an early retirement- something few dentists even dream of, let alone realize.

Back to your retirement: you now have three partners each with an equal share in the practice. You have banked about $500,000 from the sale of the partnerships over the last 6 years and you have also netted nearly $300,000 a year from the business itself. Some quick math will tell you that you have made nearly two and half million dollars in that time, while still working but phasing into retirement. Contrast that with the average dentist who simply slows down or stops taking new patients and then closes his doors and you will see how our way has been much more successful and fulfilling. You don't want all your hard work and dedication to come down to simply closing the door on a business you love, do you? With this plan, it doesn't have to. You can pretty much go out with a bang and with plenty to show for your hard work. The final step in this Profitable Partnership Plan will be to sell your share of the partnership. You can either sell it to your current partners or they can choose to bring in another partner to purchase your share in the practice.

You will want to determine a pre-assigned value to your stake in the business as the founding partner and owner of equipment and incidentals. If you own the property and did not include that as part of the partnership, you can choose to sell the property to the new practice or to charge them a fair market rent, in which case you will have yet another income generating source for your retirement.

It is truly never too soon to start planning for your retirement. You may not be planning the same way your parents did or your brother or next door neighbor is, but having a smart, lucrative exit strategy in place as early as possible will give you peace of mind and secure your future both in dentistry and beyond. The business you are building today can be the key to your financial security in retirement, but only if you know how to turn your years of effort into a profit rather than letting your business dwindle into obscurity. Use the tools we are giving you to make a positive impact on you and your family's future.

Money Trap #2 – High Cost Supplies
As we discussed in an earlier chapter, the cost of overhead is an important factor in determining your profitability in your dental practice. Your biggest expenses are definitely labor and facility costs, but keeping an eye on the small things will help you save money in the short term and add to your retirement nest egg in the long run. While we are discussing alternate ways to fund your retirement, investing for the long term is always a good idea and if you can save

money in your practice that is more money you can be putting away for retirement.

Many dentists are pressured into using sales representatives from local companies for their office and dental supplies, but careful shopping around both on the Internet and through buying clubs will quickly demonstrate that these aren't always the best deals. What is important when you are purchasing supplies is the bottom line. You may have a sales representative that you have always used, but if you are paying 15-20% more for their supplies than you could elsewhere, it's not worth the relationship.

Many sales reps will tell you that you need to purchase from their company so that you are able to get repairs done quickly, but there are many, many independent repair companies who will be eager to get your business if you have equipment that needs to be fixed. The amount of repairs you will need will not outweigh a savings of 20% on a large piece of equipment.

A buying club has the advantage of deep discounts and availability of a variety of supplies. Just think, if you are running a $500,000 practice, you could save over $4,000 a year with a 15% savings from a buying club. Over the next 10 or 15 or 20 years, that is a lot of money that could be channeled into retirement or building of your practice or both. Just by examining your costs and taking each item into careful consideration, you can free up money for your retirement and not step into another money trap!

Planning For Retirement With Another Income Source
As we learned earlier, you can treat your dental practice like the investment that it is and reap a great return on that investment when you know how to retire well. Your hard work today on building a strong and vibrant practice will pay huge dividends in the future when you are nearing retirement, but what if you could create another income stream right now, one that would grow right alongside your current practice? Sounds great, right?

Many dentists and other professionals look outside their professions for investments, possibly in real estate or in other types of businesses. Some are successful and some fail miserably, but all of them, successful or not, have to take time and energy away from their passion of dentistry to try to create an income generating business on the side. Before you get tempted to join a friend who is opening a restaurant or a car wash, ask yourself some hard questions:

- What do I know about this business?
- What do I know about the person who is asking me to join him/her?
- How much effort will I need to put into this side business?
- What do I stand to lose if the business fails?

Once you have asked and answered these questions, you will probably find that you do have some doubt about the business venture and that doubt is telling you not to move forward. It's important to listen to your own intuition when contemplating an investment and to look to others with a proven track record to see what they are doing right.

So, what business could you run simultaneously with your dental practice? According to Dr. Rich Erickson, dental assisting schools are the answer. After realizing that he would be hard pressed to achieve financial independence through his dental practice alone, Dr. Erickson decided that he needed to find another source of income besides his clinical practice. He understood that he couldn't take valuable time and energy away from his own practice and wanted to develop an endeavor that would be symbiotic with his established business. Dental assistant training fit the bill perfectly.

Dr. Erickson's ability to think outside the box has resulted in early retirement from his clinical practice, financial independence and a steady income achieved through continuing to teach and run his own dental assisting school. He also sells his system to other dentists who are interested in setting up their own dental assisting schools.

Let's take a look at how he works these schools. The educational model he developed is run right out of a current dental practice on Saturdays only. Unlike commercial dental assisting schools, the tuition for his school is just under $3,000 for a 10-week course, as compared to over $10,000 and nearly a year for traditional programs. His course, which is available for purchase, requires an initial investment of about $12,000 including all materials a... virtual turnkey school! You can benefit from his 20 years of experience in the dental assisting training field and be underway with your own school in short order.

Some of the benefits of an in-house dental assisting school are:

- Low overhead: run the school out of your current office on Saturdays when your office is closed anyway.
- Available staff: use your current dental assisting staff to run the classes. They will earn a great salary teaching and have the knowledge and experience to impact new students.
- Minimal effort on your own part: you should plan to teach a few classes each session, but it is not necessary for you to be there every week during an individual session.
- Ease of set up: the program Dr. Erickson sells is ready to go just about immediately. All the forms, manuals, paperwork, exams and other materials you need are included. You won't have to reinvent the wheel.

This opportunity isn't for everyone. Some states do require certain certifications that can only be obtained through a full time, accredited program. Most states don't require the certification, however, and you can ascertain the laws in your own state while you are researching the possibility of opening a dental assisting school.

The advantage of running this type of school is that the market for dental assistant training is strong. Many people are interested in starting a new career, especially in healthcare, but are unable to quit their current jobs while training for a new one. They also may not have the time to commit to a year or longer for training before they can begin their new career. With a Saturday only program, your students can keep their current job while learning a new trade. A simple classified advertisement in the help wanted section of your local newspaper will likely yield enough calls to fill your first class.

Dr. Erickson has had great success, both with his own school and with duplicating his process for others, so much, in fact, that he finds dentists actively seeking out his graduates above those from traditional programs. What you will find if you can implement this program is an additional source of income for your practice that is so flexible and intertwined with your current business that it will seem to be just an extension of what you are already doing rather than a side business that drains your energy and your attention from building your practice.

By now, you are probably wondering what kind of money you could be making on your own dental assisting school. After all, when you are thinking about exit strategies and retirement, what that all comes down to is money-how much will you have and how long will it last? One thing to consider when you begin this type of venture is saving for retirement. If you don't need the income from this school to keep up with your current expenses and you start while your practice is relatively young, you could be putting away a nest egg that will guarantee a comfortable and probably early retirement. Once you retire from clinical practice, you could feasibly continue to teach and live from the income that channels from the school.

Let's take an example from Dr. Erickson to see how much can be made with this model. With a 10-week course running about $2,800 in tuition and 22 students per class, you are looking at a gross income of over $60,000. Your overhead, even after paying your assistants a great wage, is just about 18%, leaving you with a profit of roughly $50,000 per session! Yes, that is not per year, it is per session. You could theoretically run 4 sessions per year for a total profit of $200,000 per year just from the dental assisting school. Your current employees will be happy to teach the classes as they will likely make more money for teaching that Saturday class than they do in a regular day of assisting.

Your students will benefit by attaining real life skills, learning in a dental office setting, from dental assistants and from you, the dentist. This won't be a theoretical class, it will be as close to on the job training as they can get. Of course, with such a condensed course of study, they will have plenty to do between Saturday classes, but it will be worth it. And, it will be worth it to your bottom line to start your own dental assisting school.

A Note About Disability
As an independent dentist, do you carry disability insurance for yourself? If you answered no, you are not alone. Most dentists have little or no provisions for what would happen if they became disabled. Social Security does provide some disability coverage, but nothing close to what your dental practice provides. By creating an alternate stream of income you are essentially making yourself disability-proof! If you are unable to continue in clinical dentistry, you can still run your school and count on a steady income. If you get disability insurance (which you absolutely should!) you can still continue with your school without interrupting your disability payments should you be unable to practice. Because the school is really outside your clinical practice, it doesn't interfere with disability benefits.

Exit Purposefully
If your head is swimming with ideas, don't be alarmed. It can be both exhilarating and overwhelming to think about retirement. There are so many variables that go into planning for the future and it is human nature to try to avoid the inevitable. Few of us really want to think about a time when we will be unable to work, but the sooner you think about it, the better your retirement will be.

If you are close to retirement, take heart! These ideas are not based on a retirement investment plan that you should have started twenty years ago; they are real steps you can take right now, today! You may find that the retirement you thought you couldn't have is now in reach and that these opportunities are just what you needed to achieve that goal!

Chapter Fourteen:

The Profitable Partnership

When you think about retirement, what kind of plans and dreams do you have? Are you thinking about having more free time to spend with your family and friends? Maybe your dream retirement involves a lot of golf or a lot of travel, or maybe just a complete change from the busy life you have now as a clinical dentist. If your retirement is still decades away, you probably haven't given it much thought at all. Your time and effort are being poured into building a practice and you can't imagine a time that you would want to give that up.

It would probably surprise you to learn that most dentists retire from practice in their late 50s or early 60s and that most of them do it the wrong way. The vast majority of dentists spend an entire career building up a practice and then end up selling it for pennies on the dollar or even worse, just letting it go when they are ready to retire. They don't realize that they are actually sitting on a goldmine and with our proven plan they could retire wealthier than they had imagined.

In the past, when dentists planned for retirement, they looked outside their own practice and profession to make the money they would need for a comfortable lifestyle once they finished working. What these doctors failed to realize was that taking all their time and effort and hard earned money and putting it in a business they knew virtually nothing about was a mistake.

Rather than invest in someone else's business, they could spend the last few years of their practice making a huge profit on the business they had already poured their heart and soul into. But you have the advantage. By learning this simple but effective strategy to profitable partnerships, you will be sprinting that last lap toward the retirement finish line, rather than limping around the last curve.

Let's break the action plan down into a few simple steps. First, you are going to build up your practice. That may seem like the opposite of what you would want to be doing, but it's for the best. Next, you are going to take on a partner, not an associate. This first partner is just the beginning and we will soon see how the program will make this one and each additional partner profitable beyond what you would have imagined. You will then take on additional partners over the next several years; you are going to set the timetable for this partnership and your retirement. It can take as long as you want it to take because you are in control.

A note here about what most dentists do: please don't be tempted into using a practice brokerage to sell your business for you. Of course, you know people who have done it; you may even have purchased your practice from one of these services. But, do yourself a favor and don't use them. They have only their commission in mind, not all the years you have worked to build a successful business out of helping people. They cannot possibly match the amount of profit you will make by using this partnership program. It may be tempting to just put this into someone else's hands and collect your money when it is all over, but if you will just explore the options of this program you will see where the real profit is. More than anything, you deserve to make a profit from the business you worked so hard to create.

Step One: Build It!

If you want to retire at age 59, you should start with the Profitable Partnership plan at least 5 years in advance of that age. Unlike the dentist who is going to start playing more golf and taking fewer appointments, you are going to work harder and smarter in these last few years. After all, you want your practice to be appealing to a potential partner as a smart investment. The better your business is doing, the more attractive it will be to potential investors. Keep marketing, keep taking new patients, keep doing all the things that have made you so successful and more. You will be able to get top dollar for your business if it is in tiptop shape.

There are a few caveats, however. This is absolutely not the time to build or purchase new office space. It may be very tempting to upgrade your building or move to that big new medical plaza that just opened, but you have to resist. Taking on new and larger expenses at this point in the business just isn't smart; you are going to be selling soon and the lower your overhead, the higher your profit. That's just good math and it makes sense. Additionally, if you haven't purchased new technology such as a Cerac or filmless or digital x-ray equipment, don't do it now. Just as you wouldn't put new pink carpeting in your living room right before you sell your home, don't make any fancy upgrades to your practice. Chances are, the new partner will come in with his or her own ideas of what types of equipment they want to use. After all, they are the ones moving forward with the practice; you are on your way out. Keeping an eye on this type of expense will benefit you in the long run.

Let's take a quick look at the numbers for this partnership program and see how it works. The math is so simple, it's astounding and it is nearly as simple to implement as it is to understand.

Dr. A. has built up his dental practice for the last 25 years. He is getting ready to retire in a few years, so he has taken on a partner, Dr. B. Dr. A. will sell half his practice to Dr. B. for one half of the amount his business collected in the last year. In this case, let's use $400,000 although most dentists are doing well over that amount. So, Dr. B. has now become an equal partner with Dr. A for the amount of $200,000. Dr. A. now has $200,000 in the bank and is still practicing dentistry and is a partner in his former solo practice. Are you with us so far?

Dr. A. and Dr. B. continue to work together for a couple of years. Two is a good rule of thumb for the time between taking on partners, but it could be a little less or much more, whatever your personal timetable requires. The two doctors work the practice during that time, continuing to build it up and work hard. When the time is right, they take on another partner, Dr. C. He will become a partner by paying one third of the value of the practice to the two doctors. That puts another $141,000 into Dr. A.'s bank account for retirement. A few more years pass and now, Drs. A., B., and C., take on a fourth partner, Dr. D. He will purchase his share of the practice for one quarter of its worth, for this example $100,000. In reality, these numbers would increase as the collections of the practice go up each year and with greater production, but for our purposes, we will keep our examples simple.

Now, Dr. A. is working much, much less than he was about five years ago. He has more time for family and for golf, but unlike his counterparts who are letting their practices fade or selling them at a loss, he has nearly a half a million dollars in the bank and he is still working!

When he decides to finally sell his stake in the practice, he will receive what is known as the "death value" for it. This would be an amount equal to 100% of the collections from the year of the partnership, in this example $400,000. Each of the three remaining partners would contribute to the buyout of Dr. A. and would become the new proprietors of the dental practice, each with a third share. Dr. A. will have $841,000 to show for the sale of his practice over the six years he has been working the profitable partnership program. In addition, he was making a yearly salary for each year he continued in the practice. If we estimate his salary at $200,000 for the first three years and $100,000 for the last three, we will see that he has made nearly two million dollars in six years! That is the profitable partnership program!

At this point, you should be running some numbers for yourself in your own head. If your practice is doing a million dollars a year in collections, you can more than double the example we shared here!

Additionally, if your salary is much higher, that will have a major impact on the numbers as well. Those brokerages don't look so good anymore, we hope!

Benefits Of The Profitable Partnership

The first and most obvious benefit to this program is, of course, financial. We all want to be compensated for our hard work and determination and when you are ready to retire from your clinical practice, you deserve to be rewarded financially for all you have done to build your practice over the years. There are also benefits that go beyond the financial.

Because you are setting up a partnership, you are still going to be operating as a true solo practice within a group. Now, you will be working fewer hours. If you are starting with a 40-hour workweek, you can expect to drop by about 40% almost immediately because you are now sharing space with your partner and you won't be solely responsible for your patients. This is a great benefit to doctors who are headed for retirement and is one of the main reasons so many dentists let their businesses slide. After bringing in a partner, your productivity will increase and your income will be protected. Even if you should suffer from a disability, you are no longer completely responsible for the income of your practice.

You can also take heart that you are finished with associates. We all know that part time associates are a good way to increase production and can be very good for the bottom line of our business. If you have been in the dental business for any length of time, you also understand the headaches that go along with setting up and keeping associates. Those days are over.

Conversely, if your practice had problems before, don't expect them to magically disappear when you take on that partner. It will actually increase any troubles exponentially, which is why it is so important to get your business running smoothly before starting the profitable partnership program.

On another front, you may feel a little bit of resentment or competition with your new partner, especially if they are much younger and are out to make changes right away. Your new partner may even be more popular with your patients, and a little animosity is to be expected. You need to keep your eye on the prize, however, which for you is retirement and a huge profit in a few years. Let your new partner take some of the glory.

Okay, you've got a partner, you are getting used to him, now what? Well, you have to keep working, keep seeking out new patients and keep building that business. One way to keep the momentum you have been working on is to attract new patients. If you were getting 25 to 50 new patients a month before, now you will have to just about double that. You may want to consider expanded hours, weekends or earlier in the day. Whatever you do to grow the business, be sure to keep your overhead no higher than 60% so that you can continue to be profitable.

Partnership Tips
- 75% of your patients should be in the recall system. If you fall below that number, be sure to bring it up before you take on a partner
- Get out of debt. Debt will be the enemy of your new partnerships. It not only reduces the amount you will be able to sell your practice for, it simply makes all the deals more complicated. If you are planning ahead for retirement, put all your focus on staying out of debt
- Accounts receivable should be no more than one month's worth of collections. If you are further behind than that, your practice won't appeal to a prospective buyer.

Real Estate
We all know that even in a volatile market, real estate is a valuable investment over time. Whether you decide to use our profitable partnership plan (which you should!) or go with a broker to sell your business (which you should not!)

you need to keep any real estate holdings out of the dealings with the partnership or sale of the practice. The inside of your dental office isn't really worth that much. Dental equipment doesn't hold its value any more than a new car does and in our type of deal, you don't need to squabble over the value of equipment or office furniture. You are being paid on the almost intangible value of your practice. Real estate will only complicate the partnership deal and keeping it separate protects your interests.

You can set the value of the real estate when you first enter the partnership and then when you are ready to retire, offer it to the remaining partners at that value. If you choose not to sell them the real estate, you could work out a rental agreement and lease them the property which would provide an income stream for years to come. Of course if you sell, you can add that to the money you already have in the bank from the partnership and that could easily double or triple the profit you have already made depending on real estate values when you retire.

Taxes And Regulations

While we believe you can enter into these partnerships and sell your practice independent of brokers, you will need the assistance of an attorney to complete all of these dealings. Your accountant will also be invaluable in these proceedings for tax purposes and determining the fair value and collections of your practice for the years preceding the partnerships. Laws differ from state to state and the tax laws are continually changing and evolving. Your accountant will be able to help you make smart decisions about how to take on the partners and even when for the best tax benefits.

Staffing

You may be ready to retire, but your staff may not be. If you are going to cut your hours down from 40 to 24, your staff will likely want to still keep their full time jobs and more importantly their full time salaries. It can be done.

The most common way is to share staff with your new partner. If you are doing Straight-6-Scheduling and the

Profitable Partnership Program, you will realize that you are doubling the capacity of your practice so your 40-hour employees will now have 48 hours of doctors' time to cover. In the case that all your employees, or even most, remain, you can hire part time staff to cover the overages.

Your working time with your new partner will be minimal since you are going to expand your open office time to accommodate your partner's working hours. Unlike with an associate, you will not be working together and sharing patient loads, you will be working separate shifts. Otherwise, as you added partners, you would need to add square footage as well. By the time you take on your final partner, your partners may be ready to expand, but you are ready to retire!

Of course, as a good manager, you realize that all of this should be covered well before you bring in a partner to the practice. You should address all your staff's concerns about their job security, salary and whatever else they may be worried about. After all, you do have their livelihood in your hands as you are working through this partnership program, it's important to remember that.

As your partnerships grow and you bring in another and maybe yet another doctor, so will your staff need to grow to meet the demands of a multiple doctor office. The staff will be office staff, not the staff of each doctor and that will help you all grow your practice together and work as a team for the common goal.

Financing And Making The Sale
You might be seeing dollar signs when you think about the numbers we have been running in our example, but maybe you are wondering where you are going to find a young dentist with five or six hundred thousand dollars who can buy into your million dollar practice. You don't have to find someone with a trust fund; you just have to understand the financing of the partnership.

Your ideal candidate for partnership will be able to provide 25% of the purchase price in liquid assets. Once that is established, you will co-sign a loan for him or her for the amount of the partnership. That may sound strange, but bear with us. The loan will never leave the bank; rather it will stay in an escrow account for the duration of a trial partnership period of 18 months. During that time, the buyer and the seller will be working as though the partnership is already in effect, paid in full. Either party may terminate the agreement during that time, but if the trial period is successful, then the loan is completed and taken out of escrow. The payment of the loan is now up to the buying partner and the seller's name is taken off the note.

Money isn't the only factor, and if you are close to retirement, you are probably already worrying what kind of a person you would select to take over your business. You will want to scrutinize any potential partners and make sure that his or her style, skills, and personality will be a good fit for your individual practice. You can't be too careful and you should be wary of being swayed by your emotions. Do a credit check, a background check, and a DEA check-they will be worth the time and expense. Your best candidate is probably a doctor who had a successful practice but had to relocate to your area.

Saying Goodbye
It may be hard to finally leave your practice, especially if you have spent decades of your life building it from the ground up. When you are finally ready to retire, you can keep a little stake in the business if you want. Some doctors choose to keep a 5% share in the practice and work in a clinical capacity when the other doctors are away or if emergencies require extra help. Some just like to keep their foot in the door, so to speak, because it is too difficult to just cut and run.

Another way of keeping an interest in the practice is the founding father's fee that is popular in other businesses. In dentistry, it's done as a percentage of the business, generally 1 or 2%. This would ensure that you, the person who founded the business, would be available for consulting on matters of marketing or help with a problem in the office. Rather than set up an awkward payment plan for your help, the compensation is built into the fee.

Hope And A Plan
So many Americans and dentists in particular, have been late to the game of saving for retirement and are now worrying and trying to catch up. Putting your time, energy and money into a business other than dentistry is an exercise in futility. You are busy and have a thriving dental business. It doesn't make sense to divert your energy from your passion of dentistry to try to make some money in a restaurant venture or worse a questionable investment club. You have your biggest investment right under your nose and if you take the advice here to heart, you will be reaping the financial rewards for years to come.

It's never too early, and it's not too late. That's the good news. Even if you are already contemplating retirement, you can put this plan into action and retire more comfortably than you ever thought possible. The same hard work and determination that got you to this point will put you over the top when it comes to making a profit from the sale of your practice. If you aren't ready to retire until you are in your eighties, that's just fine, as long as you want to continue to practice clinical dentistry. We want to make the retirement you want possible on your own terms so that you can retire when you want and have a big profit to show for it. The Profitable Partnership Program is all about making your retirement dreams a reality.

ONE FINAL THOUGHT ...

There's nothing quite like the satisfaction of creating an office that's running smooth, patients that are happy with your services, and a bottom line that is constantly growing while you're working less hours. If this sounded more like a pipe dream than a reality when you first opened this book, I hope that you have discovered that you can – and will – grow your practice with less work (and energy) by simply following the tips and strategies we've discussed. There's no need to work 12-14 hour days in order to create a practice that can survive – or even thrive – in today's economy. There are ways to streamline your practice to give you more time with your family, more energy for the things you love, and more money to use to enjoy life to the fullest and prepare for your future.

Why shouldn't you be able to enjoy your practice – and still have a life outside the office? Well, you can! All you have to do is take charge of your practice and begin to institute the strategies we've discussed to bring in more patients, make your schedule work for you, become more productive each and every day, and make more money than you every thought possible! We've given you the tools you need to get out there and move your practice to the next level – now get out there and do it! Your future as the community's leading (and best paid) dentist awaits you – go enjoy it!

Bartram Dental
Center

September 3, 2008
Dear Dr Woody Oakes:

I would like to take a moment to extend my deepest gratitude to you and the staff at Excellence in Dentistry for the personal attention I have received and for the remarkable changes in my dental practice. Last October, I went into your program with great apprehension. I was frustrated with my staff; I was working 30 hours a week; and, quite frankly, I hated dentistry and everything associated with it. My production was around $70K/month with a 90% collection ratio and I was averaging about 28 new patients a month. I realize those numbers aren't "terrible," especially for a practice that is only 3 years old. But I knew the potential of the practice was so much more, I just didn't know how to reach that potential by myself. So, I decided to hire you, Dr Woody Oakes, as my dental coach. I wasn't sure if a consultant could help my office without physically coming into the practice and seeing our daily routine. Boy, was I wrong!

So here I am, almost 12 months later, with a thriving, booming practice. The number of new patients that I average each month has risen to 60. One month we actually saw 89 new patients!!! My monthly collections average between $100K and $110K (98% - 102% collection ratio), and, get this, I have cut back my hours!! I am now only seeing patients 24 hours a week!! I use the rest of the time to do administrative items that I never had time to do, resulting in me being less stressed and having more quality time to spend with my family. I actually love going to work again. That is a statement that I thought I would never say for the remainder of my career.
Dr Oakes, words cannot express how much you have helped me as a dentist, a business owner, and a manager of people. My wife would even tell you I have become a better husband and father. Your

coaching program has given me tools and confidence to be the best dentist that I can possibly be. I do plan on continuing with your program... I would be foolish not to. And with results like these, I feel confident in recommending your coaching program. I look forward to a long-term relationship with both you and your fabulous staff.

Thanks again for all that you do!!

Sincerely,

Jason Lewis

TROY FAMILY DENTAL

Richard R. Boatman, Jr., D.M.D., P.C

506 EDWARDSVILLE ROAD - TROY, ILLINOIS 62294
PHONE (618) 667-8020 - FAX: (618) 667-8078

My practice is doing fairly well. We have deposited $2.2 million each of the last two years.

But we had flat lined and could not get to the next level. I knew we could do better but didn't know how.

Woody looked at EVERY aspect of my practice and with his help we will produce $3,000,000 this year. I made $800,000 on a $15,000 investment. What an ROI! And, I'm excited about staying on with Woody in his alumni-coaching program.

I would highly recommend Woody and his coaching program. Woody provides the best and the brightest people for all aspects of your practice management. And the staff at Excellence in Dentistry is the nicest you will ever encounter.

Thanks for everything Woody. You're the best!

Rich Boatman

Troy, Illinois

WOODLAND
FAMILY DENTAL

Cheryl Mitchell, D.D.S.

315 West Higgins Lake Drive
P.O. Box 356
Higgins Lake, MI 48627

(989) 821-9458

Woody has had the most profound impact on my career than any other dental "guru" or publication. Six years ago when I bought my partner out at 29 years old and became a solo practitioner, I was scared! I dug out my old *The Profitable Dentist* newsletters and *Driving Dentist* CD's to study them. I made a list of changes we needed to make in our practice and went to work. In 12 months I was able to collect by myself what the practice was collecting as a partnership. I doubled my collections! When I joined Woody's Coaching Club I wasn't sure there was much more to learn about managing a practice. I was wrong. Woody takes a comprehensive approach – covering every aspect of a successful practice. The past two years I have drastically decreased the hours I practice, but not by choice. I had a very difficult pregnancy followed by a newborn with health issues. Thankfully the systems we had in place allowed us to maintain our numbers. As Woody always says, "You need to do a lot of things right." It works! This year we are on track to have our best year ever despite the economy and living in one of the hardest hit states. I love my profession and owe much of my success to the ideas Woody has taught me!

Cheryl Mitchell, DDS
Cheryl Mitchell, D.D.S.

Dr. Woody Oakes is a dentist, author, entrepreneur, and lecturer. He has written 17 previous books (all in the field of dentistry) and two novels. He enjoys all sports and restoring vintage cars.

He lives with his wife "Megan" and daughter "Shelby" in Floyds Knobs, Indiana

If you would like more information on my Coaching Program please visit www.theprofitabledentist.com and click on "Coaching" or, call "us" at 1-800-337-8467.

If you are interested in participating in the Program, we will place you on a "waiting list" for next year's class and send you an application. Remember, I only work with 20 practices each year!